PLANT DRUGS THAT CHANGED THE WORLD

Books by Norman Taylor

Taylor's Encyclopedia of Gardening
Flight from Reality
Cinchona in Java
Guide to the Wild Flowers
Color in the Garden
Fragrance in the Garden
The Permanent Garden
Herbs in the Garden
The Everblooming Garden
Fruit in the Garden
Mathews' Field Book of American Wild Flowers (Revision)
Taylor's Garden Guide
The Guide to Garden Flowers
The Ageless Relicts
Narcotics: Nature's Dangerous Gift
1001 Questions Answered about Flowers
Guide to Garden Trees and Shrubs
Plant Drugs That Changed the World

PLANT DRUGS THAT
CHANGED THE WORLD

By Norman Taylor

WITH DRAWINGS BY MARGARET COSGROVE

DODD, MEAD & COMPANY · NEW YORK

Second Printing

Library of Congress Catalog Card Number: 65-18911
Printed in the United States of America
by The Cornwall Press, Inc., Cornwall, N.Y.

Acknowledgments and a Warning

It is a pleasure to acknowledge the kind help of several institutions and individuals in the preparation of this book. My especial gratitude goes to Miss Gertrude Annan, Librarian at the New York Academy of Medicine, and to Mr. Robert Jones, recently librarian at the New York Botanical Garden, now at the Massachusetts State University at Amherst. To my friend Dr. Harry Gold, professor of Clinical Pharmacology at the Cornell Medical College, who kindly read the manuscript, I am under most grateful obligation.

Among commercial firms my chief obligation is to Mr. Hans R. Schmidt, Pharmacognosist at S. B. Penick and Co., of New York; to Mr. Walter Fuhrman of Charles Pfizer and Co.; to Dr. Charles E. Lyght of Merck and Co.; to Dr. Howard H. Angell of the Upjohn Co.; to Dr. Richard H. Roberts of Ciba Pharmaceutical Co., and to Mr. Kenneth R. Hanseh of Syntex Laboratories. It is of course understood that none of these individuals or institutions is responsible for any statement in the book, the author alone accepting that obligation.

WARNING

Many remedies in this book are as innocent as tea. Others are so dangerous that they are prescribed in microscopic doses. Whether dangerous or innocuous, self-medication is always a hazard, and if illness threatens, a physician is better-equipped to deal with it than any layman.

[v

Contents

Acknowledgments and a Warning : *v*

1. Whispers from the Earth : 1

2. The Andean Miracle : 4

3. A Roaring Whisper : 19

4. The Drug Seekers : 34

5. Doctor Hosack and St. Anthony's Fire : 58

6. The Greatest Killer : 72

7. From Shen Nung to Brigham Young : 101

8. "Wilt Thou Cure Thine Heart?" : 115

9. The Potato's Lethal Cousins : 133

10. The Cathartic Racket : 152

11. The Helpful Poisoners : 171

12. The Pain-Killers : 197

13. Father Damien, Stevenson, and Joseph
     F. Rock : 219

14. Thomas Addison and Two Tropical
     Plants : 228

     Bibliography : 255

     Index : 265

PLANT DRUGS THAT CHANGED THE WORLD

1. Whispers from the Earth

THE FAINTEST WHISPERS from the earth sometimes point to Nature's deepest secrets. Evanescent as mist, reeking of the jungle, of African effluvia or even of the barnyard, who first caught her elusive messages? It is as if Nature ignored the learned and kissed the ears only of those who live close to her. How else explain why a savage people in a tropical rain forest ultimately gave us a drug that has eased the pain or saved the lives of uncounted multitudes?

Some of Nature's secrets seem so fantastic that scientists at first ignored them, but presently admitted "there might be something in it." Generally these skeptics put such rumors in the derisive category of "Sunday Supplement Science." A few of these whispers from the earth came from such remote and primitive tribes, and seemed so improbable that they slipped into obscurity, only to confound the scientists years later. Brilliant chemists and perceptive physicians, who ultimately listened to such whispers, have given us a rich battery of life-saving drugs. They would be the first to admit that jungle lore may lead to medical triumph.

Not all of Nature's secrets come from dank and sultry rain forests. Many simple country people, knowing nothing of botany, chemistry or pharmacology, have ears better tuned to catch these whispers than city folks. Rustic lore often hides for years the treasures that Nature has secreted in the roots, stem, bark, juice, leaves, flowers, fruit and seeds of plants. Some of them are now worldwide remedies. Many of them were worthless, and a few hatched a spate of fantastic quackery.

Such whispers of hope have come from nearly every country. Often the secrets of Nature's bounty were unlocked by people so simple that they never guessed that their discoveries would someday reach the floor of the Stock Exchange. Long centuries before, for no one knows how long, there must have been patient, watchful testing of hundreds of plants. How else explain the final triumph?

Among these unconscious benefactors of mankind have been Indians from Amazonian rain forests; arrow poisoners from Africa and their cousins, the ordeal poisoners; Indians from the Andes; Greek peasants; the Jesuits of Lima; a Chinese Emperor hundreds of years before Christ; a Shropshire farm woman and scores of others.

Even our dear old grandmothers had "cures" made from "simples"—hundreds of them, mostly from plants. Their reputed value has since been well exploded, even their remedy for dauncy, a "disease" of unknown cause.

But in spite of much fumbling, science has given us priceless remedies, many of them derived from the plant lore of people quite innocent of science. If their final evaluations proved their worth, these remedies are now in the *United States Pharmacopœia* or the *National Formulary,* which are the bibles of all American physicians. They have long since left the jungle, are dispensed by every doctor and made by huge pharmaceutical companies who charge more for them than many think is fair.

Such accredited remedies ought to have driven quackery

out of the country. But the will to believe in some magical cure still costs the public millions of dollars, because they do not know that the magic is imaginary. But who will not seek a remedy for the agony of gout, for the heart that flutters too much, for the misery of malaria, for a distraught mind, for the pain of arthritis or a dozen other ills?

The primitive hunt for real remedies has gone on for at least nineteen hundred years, and maybe much longer, for we read of an Egyptian doctor in 1600 B.C. giving paregoric to "prevent the excessive crying of children." Today these drugs are mostly derived from a laboratory, but what the scientists and their primitive progenitors strive for is a *specific*. Of real specifics there are not too many derived from plants. A recent medical dictionary defines a specific as "a remedy especially indicated for any particular disease."

The story of specifics and other remedies derived from plants is thus the record of centuries of trial and error. It deals with whispers from the earth now in every drugstore. For the specialist the origin and use of these life-saving or pain-killing drugs is buried in rather voluminous books, lumped under the general heading of *Materia Medica*. These invaluable records make heavy going for most of us, for they are crammed with the jargon of the botanist, the technicalities of the pharmacologist, the language of the doctors and the terrifying terminology of the chemist.

But under such daunting complexities lies the history of man's ultimate conquest of many diseases. Where such plants were found, who first used them and how they reached us constitute the story of our emergence from what one pharmacologist called the "frailties of our existence."

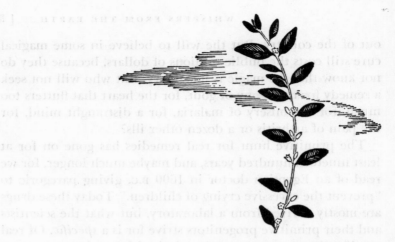

Andean shrub that yields cocaine

2. The Andean Miracle

ABOUT A HUNDRED MILES SOUTH of Lima and near the Pacific Coast of Peru there was found the most famous textile ever to come from South America. It is the fabulous Paracas Textile dating from about A.D. 500 and made by some unknown pre-Inca genius, about six or seven centuries before the Incas reached what is now Peru. Its gorgeous coloring, fine design and superb material have been the envy of the experts who ascribe it to the Nazca period of Peruvian history, which flourished from some years before the birth of Christ to about A.D. 500.

There is no method of pin-pointing a precise date to this world-famous fabric, as it may well be older than A.D. 500. Its history, however, is fairly clear, for it was wrapped around the body of a mummified potentate who was buried in a funeral urn in almost regal splendor. His knees were hunched up in the fetal posture common to many early Peruvian burials—especially if the body was of an important priest, noble or king. His head was banded with an embroidered fillet, and his hair covered with golden ornaments.

In those days, and even after the arrival of the Incas, it was obligatory to provide sustenance for the departed on his way to heaven. In the bottom of the urn were placed a few ears of corn and several small bags of coca leaves. This is the earliest record of the use of coca leaves, which, with their derivatives, were destined to go all over the world, but only after a delay of nearly eighteen hundred years.

Coastal Peru at that time had reached a high degree of culture, to judge by fabrics like the Paracas Textile, their ceramics, palaces and fortifications. But their cities were on a coastal plain in the midst of one of the most absolute deserts in the world and many inhospitable miles from any source of coca, which only grows and is still cultivated on the Amazonian face of the Andes. Today it is easy to go by car from Lima, across the sterile desert, up the incredible escarpment of the western Andes, across the bleak, treeless, fearfully high Alti-Plano, over the eastern Andes and down to the hot, steaming jungle found on the Amazonian face of that gigantic mountain range. The passes wind among snow-capped peaks, and what are now roads were mere trails eighteen hundred years ago, and maybe years before that.

Over those trails sturdy natives, long before A.D. 500, must have carried bags of coca leaves from the steaming Yungas, up over the "eyebrow of the mountains" and down to coastal Peru, a distance of only three hundred miles. To a weary foot traveler, laden with coca and trudging over the terrifying topography of the Andes, it no doubt seemed much more. Why he carried these precious leaves is the basis of this chapter.

It is obvious that if Peruvian burial urns were furnished

with coca leaves as early as A.D. 500, the plant must have been well known long before that, and its use as a stimulant as much appreciated then as it is today by many millions of people. Much later, with the advent of the Incas, about A.D. 1100, we glean what coca meant to the Indians who mostly lived and still live on the Alti-Plano with an average elevation of 12,000-13,000 feet.

Soon after the Spanish conquest of 1531-36 there are innumerable records of the grandeur of the Inca capital at Cuzco. Two of the most important were by remarkable young Spanish chroniclers. One of these was a young soldier, Pedro de Cieza de Leon, who landed at Cartagena, scrambled up the Andes and joined the forces of Pizarro in the conquest of Peru. He was there between 1532 and 1550, and his *Chronica del Peru,* published at Seville in 1553, is crammed with Inca history—and with the story of coca and the potato, the latter then confined to the Alti-Plano.

The other chronicler was Garcilasso de la Vega, whose opportunity to know the Incas was unique. His father was one of the trusted officers of Pizarro and his mother an Inca princess. Their child, Garcilasso, learned from his mother the incredible lore, legend and true history of the Incas and, incidentally, about coca.

The Incas had no written language but for centuries used a knotted string, each knot commemorating some event in their history. With these knotted strings they tolled off verbally the chief events, and from them has come a fairly authentic chronology of the rise and fall of the Incas. Garcilasso wrote all this down in his *Royal Commentaries of the Incas,* issued in 1609.

Both these books are packed with coca history. We read, for instance, of a very simple Indian marriage ceremony, where the boy and girl are united without benefit of the Church. He brings a few bags of coca leaves to the girl's mother, does some household chores for the old people, and in a few days walks off with his bride. They go to a house and farm supplied by the government, which owned all the land. The farm might be only a few acres and the house, without a chimney, had only a hole in the roof to let out the smoke from the corner fireplace. But here the young couple could set up housekeeping without any expense. The government, of course, meant the Great Inca, who lived in such gorgeous splendor as to astound the Spaniards. These Inca rulers had such complete control of life, marriage, inheritance and taxation that modern dictators seem a little like naïve amateurs.

When Pizarro and his one hundred eighty men reached Cuzco, he conquered an Inca empire that stretched from Venezuela to central Argentina, plus a slice of northern Chile. There was a fabulous amount of gold and silver at the capital, but the Incas used both only for their gorgeous and very elaborate ornaments. They never had any money or coinage, as all the extensive trade was by barter. In all the markets, coca leaves were valuable evidences of wealth.

Nearly everybody was chewing these leaves, for not long before the conquest, coca was permitted to slip from being mostly a privilege of the court to the common Indians. But there had been much illegal coca chewing before the court made it legal.

In spite of its general use at the time of Pizarro's arrival, coca still retained some of its deeply religious significance. So sacred was it that Inca deities were propitiated with burnt offerings of coca leaves—usually in most impressive ceremonies. And the Inca Roca (1250-1315) conquered a part of the Amazonian face of the Andes, well knowing that it was the only part of his vast territory where coca could be grown.

One of the later Incas, just before the Spanish conquest, set up a work timetable for everyone from birth to sixty years of age. Number six of that schedule specifies that a coca picker must be a male between sixteen and twenty years of age. To-day most pickers are women and children, and they are very busy people, for everyone in the Andes knows of the amazing ability of coca leaves to relieve fatigue, promote endurance and make its users feel better.

Besides its universal chewing by modern Indians, coca was considered by Inca "physicians" as the most highly prized plant of their fabulous empire. Philip Means, no coca adherent, writes in his scholarly *Ancient Civilizations of the Andes:*

> To them it was the greatest blessing derived from the vegetable kingdom for it removed them from much anguish. . . . Its use, in ancient times, was strictly controlled by the state, but there was a widespread appreciation of the various medicinal uses of the cuca [coca] plant. It seems, on the whole, to have been a benefit to mankind, but one full of danger because of the ease with which it can be abused.

This, of course, was not the first warning about the dangers of chewing coca leaves. Some of the early ecclesiastics fretted about it, particularly its use in burial urns. Why, asked one of the padres, provide for eternity with a few coca leaves, "as if hell was so very far off"? But the Church modified its strictures, since by 1550 the clergy and cathedral at Cuzco were mostly supported by taxing coca.

At the rich mines at Potosí the Spaniards bought about two and a half million pounds of coca leaves annually to pep up their Inca slaves. And by 1548 the Spanish loot was millions of dollars annually, quite literally extracted with coca.

Today anyone can wander over much of Peru and Bolivia and see the natives chewing coca, just as they must have been doing for close to eighteen hundred years. In their toilsome journeys up the slopes of the Andes they stop, every hour or so, to renew their supply. They call the pause a *cocada,* the time when the effects of the last chew have worn thin. With the leaf they put a bit of alkali, roll it up into a quid and begin chewing it. Their mouths look as though they were holding a large marble on one side. They never swallow the quid, but so popular is coca-chewing today that in Peru and Bolivia it takes over 20 million pounds annually to keep the mountain Indians happy. Its use along the coast is more restricted, perhaps not more than 5 million pounds.

Such figures are staggering to those who have never seen these sturdy, apparently tireless Indians. They carry their loads, mostly with a tumpline, over incredible declivities with practically no food or water. And they stop only for the cocada. So well was this known to the Spaniards that they encouraged the cultivation of coca and, of course, taxed it.

As to the dangers of coca-chewing, there are at least two schools of thought. One would have it that the Indian who chews regularly can be recognized by:

His uncertain step, general apathy, sunken eyes, trembling lips, green and crusted teeth and excessively fetid breath.—*Dispensatory of the United States of America,* 24th edition, page 1405.

There are, on the other side of the fence, two well-known Peruvian physicians, Drs. C. Gutirrez-Noriega and V. Z. Ortiz, who in a recent study of coca-chewing among Indians of the Alti-Plano have suggested that these abnormally large-lunged people, living at high altitudes, do not suffer from but may be helped by coca-chewing. It causes increased heart rate, increased arterial blood pressure and an increase in the number of respirations.

To the Indians such conflicting views must seem a little pointless. These sturdy and direct descendants of the Incas well know that coca was considered divine for centuries before the Spaniards arrived, that sacrifices were made with coca leaves and that for eighteen hundred years it has been a symbol of strength. Can so many millions of people be so completely wrong for so many centuries? And they well know that on the escutcheon of modern Peru there is a coca leaf—a symbol of the endurance of the Incas.

Rumors of such an extraordinary plant soon reached Spain, and in 1565 Nicolas Monardes of Seville made what is probably the first scientific reference to coca. He repeated all that Cieza de Leon had told him and incidentally included a description of the plant that produced it and described how it is grown. Modern observers can scarcely improve on Monardes.

The plant is native in Peru and Bolivia, growing mostly between elevations of 2,000 and 8,000 feet, on the moist, steaming slopes of the Amazonian face of the Andes. Rainfall is generally from 80-150 inches a year, and the region is fit for little else, except for the culture of the tree that yields quinine. Coca would naturally be a shrub 6-8 feet high, but for ease of picking is kept at just over three feet. Normally the leaves are picked about three or four times a year. The plant is grown in *cocals,* which are small plantations of two or three acres. Some cocals are incredibly ancient; Garcilasso de la Vega inherited one from his Inca mother which had been in continuous production for four hundred years before the conquest and is still producing—a record of eight hundred years of continuous culture.

Picking coca leaves, which are about the size and texture of privet leaves, is still a colorful spectacle. The shrub is grown in narrow trenches cut in the mountainside which, from the valley beneath, seem like the seats of a vast amphitheater, lost finally in the luminous haze of the cloud-capped summit. Scattered along the trenches are hundreds of women and children, ablaze in their colorful Inca costumes, busily picking the leaves, which, after drying, are sold in every market in Ecuador, Peru and Bolivia.

Coca, of course, finally caught the attention of botanists

and was properly christened in Latin as *Erythroxylon Coca*, the first name from the Greek meaning red wood (true of some species) and *Coca* (or cuca) having always been the local name for the plant. Today the *United States Pharmacopœia* specifies that the drug derived from this Andean shrub must come from *Erythroxylon Coca* "or other species of *Erythroxylon*."

Coca Reaches Paris

Ever since the colorful histories of Garcilasso and Cieza de Leon, people in Europe wondered what there was in the leaf of coca that killed fatigue, increased endurance and made the Indians so sturdy on those fearfully high plains. Some were frankly skeptical, thinking that the young chroniclers had pulled a long bow. But how could Europe ignore the learned Jesuit, Joseph de Acosta, whose *Natural History of the Indies* became a classic? It was published at Seville in 1590, and in it Father Acosta had this to say to those who thought coca was unnecessary, and its virtues imaginary, or advocated its destruction:

For my part, and to speak the truth, I persuade not myself that it is an imagination, but contrariwise I think it works and gives force and courage to the Indians, for we see the effects which cannot be attributed to imagination, so as to go some days without meat, but only a handful of Coca, and other like effects.

There was scarcely any other chronicler more respected than Acosta, who lived in Peru from 1569 to 1583. His trained intelligence and wide learning shine through all his writings. But Europe practically ignored him, and coca was all but neglected for nearly three hundred years after Acosta died.

Finally, in 1872, there appeared a small article entitled *La*

Coca du Pérou in an obscure therapeutic journal in France, followed in 1878 and 1888 by two volumes on the history and especially on the uses of the leaves of coca. All were published at Paris by a then unknown young chemist. He was Angelo Mariani, who was born in the beautiful and romantic seaport of Bastia in the northern part of Corsica. He came by his interest in chemistry through an ancestry of physicians and chemists, and he ultimately made coca the rage of Paris. Not, of course, without several years of experimental mixing, but he finally announced the manufacture of Mariani's Coca Wine, followed by coca lozenges, tea, pastilles and other coca products. All of these consisted of elixirs or powders made from coca leaves, of which he became the largest importer in Europe.

His success was dazzling, for his coca wine went all over Europe. The Pope used it and presented a medal of appreciation to Mariani. Musicians like Gounod, Fauré, Massenet and Thomas, all sang its praises, and even royalty used it, so that Mariani prospered accordingly.

At Neuilly on the Seine he built what became the best coca museum in the world. Attached to it were conservatories in which he grew thousands of coca plants, mostly for experimental purposes. Ten of these plants reached the New York Botanical Garden at the beginning of this century, for Mariani offered them to any botanical garden equipped to care for them.

What the Pope, the public, the composers and royalty got from coca wine was much more than the kick from the wine itself. Mariani put into it a measured dose of an elixir of coca leaves, which did for the sophisticated Europeans what it had done for the Incas centuries before. Exaltation of spirit, freedom from fatigue, and a sense of well-being—it is little wonder that Mariani's Coca Wine made his fortune.

Some have dubbed him a quack, but his last volume, entitled *La Coca et ses applications therapeutiques,* was translated into English and published in New York in 1896. Perhaps a fair appraisal would be that he knew more about coca than anyone else in Europe, was a shrewd advertiser, a skillful propagandist and reaped a handsome reward. He was certainly the only one in Europe who made coca known to the world after three hundred years of neglect.

Coca Comes to Atlanta, Georgia

Long before Coca-Cola became a worldwide beverage, two essential ingredients of it were the leaves of coca and the kola nut from Africa. But early in the present century a vigilant government suggested to its manufacturers, the Coca-Cola Company of Atlanta, that they omit coca from the beverage on the ground that coca was harmful. Neither the Indians of Peru nor Mariani of Paris could understand why the United States wanted to smirch the fair name of coca, born in the high purity of the Andes and with centuries of use behind it.

After much legal wrangling the company was forced to omit coca from its beverage, which it has been doing ever since. Some years later this omission led to an amusing battle between the company and another department of the United States government. The federal officials claimed that as there was no coca in the beverage it was misleading to retain the name Coca-Cola. But the precious title had been amply protected by copyright and trademark and the public knew it so well that "Coke" became a household word.

The legal skirmishing was profound and very expensive, but the company finally won on the ground that whether or not it contained coca, *Coca-cola* was part of the language and could not be destroyed by any government.

The Essence of Coca

While no mystery surrounded the effects of coca, the fundamental ingredient of it baffled science for close to four hundred years. What could be in the juice of this miraculous leaf? Morphine had been extracted from opium, quinine from cinchona bark, and several other plant alkaloids were well known. But coca resisted all analysis until 1855.

In that year and in 1860 two German organic chemists changed the whole history of coca. One of them, a Dr. Gaedeke, announced that he had isolated the active ingredient of coca leaves, and called his discovery *cocaine*. It was a remarkable technical feat, followed four years later by the work of Dr. Niemann, who improved the discoverer's technique. Cocaine thus became available to science about the time of the American Civil War.

At first it was almost ignored, as the dosage was not yet standardized, and in improper doses it was dangerously toxic. Doctors were afraid of it or else regarded it as an uncertain remedy for what? Beyond the wonderful power of coca leaves to banish fatigue, what were the indications for the use of the pure essence of coca? Cocaine was too dangerous to give internally, its external use was limited, and it cured no disease.

For a quarter of a century the future of cocaine was uncertain. But in 1884 came an electrifying announcement from Vienna by a young doctor working in the clinic of Dr. Sigmund Freud. During Dr. Freud's absence from Vienna his assistant, Dr. Carl Koller, astounded the world of eye specialists with a statement that was to revolutionize eye surgery. Dr. Koller was then just twenty years old.

He and his associates had been working with dilute solutions of cocaine, and one day he put a drop or two on the tip of his tongue. Tastelessness and insensibility followed almost immediately, but not for long. This led to experiments on frogs and guinea pigs, which ultimately made Dr. Koller world-famous. He had long known that operations on the eye, especially the removal of cataracts, were an excruciating ordeal, for no general anesthetic was then safe in such a delicate procedure. He had heard many screaming patients at the Vienna hospital, and this, plus his experience with cocainized frogs and guinea pigs, set him thinking.

Again experimental animals were used to demonstrate what he dared not try on a human patient. Using a weak solution of cocaine, he put a drop or two in the eye of a guinea pig. Even rather rough probing of that eye brought no response. It was clear to him that cocaine was a safe local anesthetic. There was not a doctor in the world who had not been clamoring for just such a tool.

The next step was Dr. Koller's determination to try it on a patient scheduled for the removal of a cataract. Before his astonished and much older colleagues, the cataract was removed painlessly, with cocaine as the local anesthetic. His final triumph came with the reading of his paper before the Ophthalmological Society of Heidelberg on September 15, 1884. He could not afford the trip from Vienna and the paper was read by another physician. Its publication all over the world made Dr. Koller justifiably famous, and he finally went to New York and practiced there until 1941.

The implications of cocaine as a local anesthetic were so great that doctors and surgeons all over the world were using it to immobilize various parts of the body besides the eye. Painless operations on the throat, the removal of bullets from a wounded hand or leg—there are dozens of emergencies that do not require ether but demand a purely local anesthetic to ensure a painless procedure. Next to the discovery of ether it was the greatest boon to the operating surgeon. No one today can realize the agonies of countless patients who were operated on before Koller discovered the amazing pain-killing power of this essence of the leaf of coca.

The isolation of cocaine prompted a search for what other ingredients might be in the leaf and for exactly how much cocaine was to be expected in any batch of coca leaves. It was found that most leaves contained only about 1 per cent of cocaine and many of them considerably less.

The average chew of the Peruvian Indians is about two ounces of the dried leaves per day. Taking 0.80 per cent as the average cocaine content of his daily dose means that the Indian absorbs about 69/100 of a grain per day. Considering that six to eight grains per day is the usual dose of a cocaine addict, and that it takes slightly over fifteen grains to be lethal, the Indian's intake of cocaine is rather moderate. And so was Mariani's Coca Wine.

The isolation of cocaine, while a boon to mankind, was ultimately to become a curse because of a large illicit market for it among cocaine addicts. These unfortunates well know that it must not be swallowed, but is directly absorbed by the mucous membranes, especially in the nose. They call the white, innocent-looking powder "snow," and when they are under the influence of it delight in the term "snowbird."

Its effects are remarkable, but its continued use by the addict is devastating. At first there is the marked stimulating effect on the higher levels of the brain, and the addict has increased mental and physical power. It was not for nothing that Conan Doyle had the immortal Sherlock Holmes use cocaine to solve the mysteries of this greatest figure in detective fiction.

But its continued use brings misery and occasional death. The determined addict ends up by believing he has sand under his skin, that insects are crawling over his body and that some baleful person is determined to do him in. One such addict, caught by the authorities, put it in a nutshell when he remarked, "If you aren't nuts before you use it, you sure are after."

The misuse of cocaine is thus another illustration of the perversity of mankind in turning one of Nature's beneficent gifts into a worldwide curse—just as was done with morphine. This lies outside the scope of this book, but has been treated in *Narcotics: Nature's Dangerous Gifts,* issued by Dell in 1963.

The Sequel

In spite of its phenomenal power as a local anesthetic, there was always the toxicity of cocaine to worry the doctors. Also, in the proper and safe dilutions of it, the effects did not last long enough. Such a challenge sparked a long search by a group of brilliant scientists for something better than cocaine.

After a long series of analyses, hundreds of experiments on animals and many failures, word came from Germany, early in the present century, that perhaps they were on the track of a real substitute for cocaine. At first the hunt had been for the extraction of other active ingredients of coca leaves. Failing in this, they tested many other plants, some of them relatives of coca but many others quite unrelated. Nothing came of this, even after months of work.

These failures stimulated Dr. Albert Einhorn to look elsewhere—not for a plant alkaloid like cocaine, but for a man-made, laboratory-hatched drug having the same results as cocaine or even better effects. Such a search today is a commonplace when wholly synthetic drugs are almost tailored in the laboratory for predictable effects. After much painstaking research Dr. Einhorn announced his discovery of just such a laboratory-hatched, wholly synthetic substitute for cocaine. It was immediately patented by the manufacturer, for whom Dr. Einhorn worked, under the name Novocain. This is a trademarked term for procaine.

Procaine (Novocain) has almost completely replaced co-caine as a local anesthetic. Everyone who visits a dentist is thankful for its pain-killing properties, and its use is now worldwide. Its final and most spectacular use is now in spinal anesthesia. Injections between the lower vertebrae into the spinal fluid completely deaden sensation in all parts of the body below the point of injection. And the effects of procaine can be made to last for prolonged operations, so that this purely synthetic drug is better than cocaine.

Such a priceless boon was thus quite literally born in a burial urn. Without the discovery of the Paracas Textile and the coca leaves in the urn, we had no way of knowing that this miracle of the Andes was so ancient and so widely used and for what purposes. With the conquest of Peru came the talented chroniclers who told us much more. No longer a mere whisper from the earth, coca became well known in Spain, but was soon forgotten. Three hundred years later the enterprising Mariani gave it such a boost that it was known all over Europe.

But the secret and precious ingredient that makes coca what it had been for eighteen hundred years eluded the scientists for centuries. The final isolation of cocaine, the synthesis of procaine and its ultimate world usage—could there be a more convincing illustration of how a faint whisper from an earth-bound burial urn might someday link Inca lore with modern medicine?

The Indian shrub that gave us reserpine

3. A Roaring Whisper

Hamlet: "How came he mad?"
First Clown: "Faith, e'en with losing his wits."

FOR OVER TWENTY CENTURIES Western science chose to ignore a very faint whisper from the earth of India. That elusive emanation floated in the tropical air for so long that Indians were as surprised as we that our medical profession and their patients now gratefully use over forty million prescriptions a year of a drug once known only to medicine men, bazaar-keepers and Indian peasants.

The original whisper was faint, largely incorrect and drenched in the superstition and ignorance of desperately poor people. Their poverty then as even today was a nightmare. No wonder these conditions result in a few cases of madness and many more of those mentally ill unfortunates who suffer from disorientation, a loss of contact with reality,

[19

and the misery of a split personality for which Eugen Bleuler coined the term schizophrenia, often called dementia prae-cox. As one walks today along any Indian road, thick with dust, filth and cattle, it is not the magical temples and tombs that rivet the attention, but the teeming millions of the underprivileged, nearly all walking. Among them is an appreciable proportion of the mentally ill.

It was for these that the drug was widely used in India. There are old records of its ancient name of Sarpagandha and Chandrá, the latter meaning "moon" and referring to its use in "moon disease," *i.e.,* lunacy. With such an outlandish name and a poor press, it is little wonder that the West never heard of it, or if they did, promptly ignored it. Its other and much more general use was as an antidote for snakebite and the sting of scorpions. It was also regarded as a remedy for malaria, but is now known to be ineffective in this greatest of Indian scourges.

The first Western scientists to pay much attention to the drug were two Dutchmen who, in 1887 and 1890, published their accounts of the plant from which it was derived and the first note on its chemistry and pharmacology. The plant was cultivated in the botanical garden at Buitenzorg, Java, then the finest tropical garden in the world. Their reports were practically ignored for over forty years, but to Drs. J. F. Eykman and M. Greshoff is due the credit of telling Western science about the identity and use of *Rauwolfia serpentina.*

Since then, hundreds of papers have been published on the drug and its source, and it soon transpired that our ignorance was even more abysmal and ancient than that of India. Actually *Rauwolfia* as a genus of plants, without any medical significance, had been properly named by Charles Plumier, a French naturalist, as early as 1703. He called it *Rauwolfia* in honor of his colleague, Leonhart Rauwolf, a German who traveled widely in the Near East. And in 1755, G. E. Rumpf,

a doctor in Amboina, published what is probably the first illustration of *Rauwolfia serpentina,* the specific name being
derived from its reputed efficacy in snakebite. He published
this in his *Herbarii Amboinensis,* which was issued at Amsterdam. On the title page he described himself as "Med. Doct.
of Hanau, Venerable Merchant and Consul to Amboina, re-
nowned as the Pliny of India and illustrious Member of the
Academic Society of Natural Philosophers of Germany." No
one should be misled by this bombastic puff, for Rumpf was
a learned Dutch botanist, and we can thank him for being one
of the first to elaborate the story and to illustrate the then
all but unknown *Rauwolfia serpentina.* Today it is one of the
best known of medicinal plants.

As the story of *Rauwolfia* finally reached its climax, all
since about 1940, it has become apparent that the genus comprised at least eighty different species, distributed over much
of the tropical Old World, and with a few found in Central
America and northern South America. All belong to the dogbane family (Apocynaceae), a group already famous for yielding ouabain, physostigmine and other drugs derived from
arrow poisons.

So far as modern sources are concerned, the outstanding
plant is still *Rauwolfia serpentina,* an evergreen subshrub,
rarely over a yard high, with a tapering, bitter root about ten
inches long. This is native in India, Ceylon, and the East
Indies, but India is the chief source of supply. Only the roots of
the plant are of any medical value. Some enthusiasts have suggested its cultivation in warm regions as a garden plant, as its
dense cluster of small pink or white flowers makes it "a very
fine ornamental shrub, something like an *Azalea.*"

Another source of the drug is *Rauwolfia vomitoria,* a shrub
of the former Belgian Congo, but supplies of this depend
upon settlement of many problems in that strife-torn country.
Still a third source is *Rauwolfia tetraphylla,* long but incor-

rectly known as *Rauwolfia heterophylla*. This shrub grows from southern Mexico to Ecuador and is common in Guatemala, where I first ran across it almost accidentally.

In December, 1938, I was on a relatively unheralded expedition to Guatemala to look over some *Cinchona* plantations, reputedly started by a large American pharmaceutical firm eager to break the Dutch monopoly of quinine. After having spent considerable time at remote plantations in that very mountainous and colorful country, I arrived back at Guatemala City and was handed a cablegram. It was from the Cinchona Instituut at Amsterdam and read, "Please collect one hundred pounds of chalchupa." Solving that puzzle took a day or two, but it turned out that chalchupa was the native name of *Rauwolfia tetraphylla,* the only American species of any medical interest.

My Dutch colleagues must have heard that chalchupa was used by the Indians as an antidote for the bite of the fer-de-lance and the coral snake, both of them common and dangerous in Guatemala. And the plant was then reputedly valuable in malaria, but that is now an exploded myth. They also knew that chalchupa (*Rauwolfia tetraphylla*) was related to the *Rauwolfia serpentina* of India, and hence possibly good for the "moon disease" (lunacy).

The chalchupa was secured from a sugar plantation called Ingenio Mirandilla, near Escuintla, which is not far from the Pacific Coast. It grows about 4-7 feet high, is common in stony river bottoms and is confined to elevations of less than 1,500 feet. No one at Escuintla ever heard of its use in madness, and subsequent investigation at the Department of Agriculture at Guatemala and talks with several doctors confirmed this.

It would be fascinating but dangerous to figure out how these stolid descendants of the Mayans, with their obvious Mongolian features, ever hit upon the fact that their native chalchupa was good for snakebite. They certainly did not know that chalchupa is first cousin to *Rauwolfia serpentina,* a plant that grows thousands of miles from them, and that it had been used for snakebite in India for twenty centuries. Perhaps such things arise spontaneously. How otherwise account for the Eurasian swastika being found on the Mayan buildings at Chichén Itzá?

Finding *Rauwolfia* in Guatemala in 1938 seems like ancient history, but only half a dozen European scientists had published anything on the plant up to that time and only one Mexican, J. Roca, and Erwin Deger had even mentioned *Rauwolfia tetraphylla.* The one hundred pounds of this plant were sent to Amsterdam in January, 1939, and nothing more was heard of it for the next few years—until *Rauwolfia* sprang into prominence.

Again, Indian doctors and pharmacologists were ahead of Western science in trying to determine the real value of *Rauwolfia.* Before 1939 they published several papers on the drug, three of the most important investigators being Drs. R. N. Chopra, N. N. Das and S. N. Mukherjee. They little realized that within a few years papers on *Rauwolfia* would be numbered in the hundreds.

No one knew better than these distinguished Indian scientists that all the early work on *Rauwolfia* was hampered by lack of knowledge of the active constituents of the root. They were forced to appraise its value with the same handicaps that were inherent in the native use of the plant—pure empiricism. They had some guidance as to its therapeutic value, mostly derived from twenty centuries of native experience with it.

The crude Indian drug consisted only of a powder ground up from the dried root, and they soon found that plants from different parts of India had varying degrees of efficacy. They were, in other words, just as blind as the doctors who used crude cinchona bark for two centuries before the isolation of quinine in 1820. But Indian medicine men had been using the ground root for mentally ill patients for centuries. In 1943, Dr. R. N. Chopra published an account of the resins found in the root, and their hypnotic and sedative effects. It was a learned attempt to pin down the basis of the cures which less well-trained people in India had long taken for granted.

The natives used it regularly for those with "moon disease," and for snakebite. In the mentally ill patients who were taking the drug regularly, it was found, purely as a side effect, that their blood pressure was noticeably reduced. It was this combination of desirable effects that sparked continued interest in this ancient remedy. It was still unknown why or how it acted, but such a challenge was to have a dramatic sequel within a few years.

In 1952, *Rauwolfia* became front-page news with the discovery by Drs. J. M. Müller, E. Schlittler and H. J. Bein of the most important of the twenty alkaloids found in the root of the Indian plant. They named it *reserpine*. Scarcely any recent medical discovery has touched off such a spate of clinical research. Here, for the first time in two thousand years, physicians had a pure alkaloid, of which they could give a measured dose with predictable effects. This has since benefited millions of patients, all over Europe and in the United States. The United States is admitting to mental hospitals the incredible number of a quarter of a million annually. For many of them reserpine makes life almost tolerable.

The great bulk of these mentally ill patients are schizophrenics. This disease of the split personality has often dangerous, violent and even suicidal manifestations. No one knows its cause and various "explanations" that it results from some deficiency in "body chemistry" leave most psychiatrists a little impatient. One modern medical textbook perhaps comes nearer the truth when it says: "No constant or characteristic structural or biochemical change has yet been established in this condition." It goes on to quote the fact that 15-20 per cent of first admissions to mental hospitals and 60 per cent of their permanent population suffer from schizophrenia.

Before the advent of reserpine, such hospitals were a nightmare to normal visitors and an agonizing terror to the inmates. For years it was known to the doctors that a sudden, violent shock administered to these unfortunates would, if it did not cure them, at least give them relief and certainly make them easier to manage and far less violent. Three different methods were used. One involved the injection of metrazol, which produced instant convulsions or epileptic-like seizures. Another was the electro-shock method where the patient had to withstand a dose of electricity just short of permanent damage. The third involved the injection of relatively large doses of insulin. The reactions to these were terrifying and so violent that some patients, in the midst of convulsive spasms, would break their bones.

Much of this dreadful therapy has been abandoned in most modern mental hospitals, due to the marvelous action of reserpine on the central nervous system and the brain. Its sedative effects are truly extraordinary, especially when combined with chlorpromazine, a wholly synthetic drug, devised in the Rhone-Poulenc Specia Laboratories in France. It was thought for some time that curare would be the drug of choice for such patients.

The plight of schizophrenic patients is bad enough if diagnosed in youth, or in its earlier stages among older people. Generally they are confined to mental hospitals and their number can be gauged by the fact that federal, state and city mental hospitals cost the United States taxpayer over three billion dollars annually. The more advanced cases must be hospitalized, often for life. Some were partially "cured" by a simple operation (lobotomy) on the brain, but such patients were never the same after, for as one observer notes with horror, "It creates a defect that can never be repaired. It places the patient once and for all beyond the reach of psychotherapy. It invariably 'down-grades' the individual, coarsening his behavior, destroying his insight, blunting his ambitions, dulling his appreciations."—(Robert S. de Ropp in *Drugs and the Mind*) In spite of these defects, lobotomy still has its adherents, who point out that without it we might be asking the question, "Of what use are these raging, miserable beings to society in their present state?"

Rauwolfia has changed most of this. That faint whisper from the earth of India, at least twenty centuries old, now roars throughout the medical world. And on such a scale that the plant is now cultivated in India, for fear the failure of wild supplies may threaten the continuance of such valuable therapy. Its derivative, reserpine, has opened up such a humane and effective procedure that some schizophrenics are so much relieved that they can return home.

Reserpine (it has several propietary names) is without much doubt the most valuable tranquilizing drug ever to come from the world of plants. Perhaps the reader should be spared a peep into one of these mental hospitals. But to understand the boon that reserpine has been we cannot ignore the fact that formerly many of these patients were murderously violent, dangerous to themselves, to other patients and to the staff, incapable of co-operation with psychiatrists eager to help them, and usually they had to be confined in rooms from which all chances of suicide were removed. Many of such patients, and nearly all of the milder cases, are now under reserpine therapy (or reserpine with chlorpromazine). They are often released from solitary confinement, allowed the privilege of a general ward, and some of them walk freely over the grounds. Such a boon has revolutionized the institutional treatment of schizophrenics.

It would be pleasant to record that reserpine has no dangers and no side effects, but it has both, so that it must be prescribed only by a doctor who understands its superlative value and its contraindications. Dr. Nathan S. Kline and his associates at the Rockland State Hospital, Orangeburg, New York, have pointed out that there are at least twenty-five side reactions of reserpine which the physician must look out for. Some of them are minor and disappear spontaneously, but others need the intervention of additional drugs or even temporary withdrawal of reserpine. One of the side effects is a marked reduction in blood pressure, "where the physician (in contrast to the patient) began feeling concerned." In such cases corrective drugs have to be administered.

The spectacular success of reserpine in the treatment of institutionalized schizophrenics should not disguise the fact that it is not a cure for that disease. This is clearly shown in those schizophrenics who have been hospitalized for many years. When the drug is stopped, most of them relapse quickly. In the less serious cases, who are sufficiently normal after treatment to be candidates for release from the hospital, the doctors are apt to keep them in the institution for a month or more without any reserpine. If there is no evidence of relapse, such lucky patients can go home, and subsequent follow-up reveals that many of them lead useful if restricted lives. A few can fill jobs requiring concentration and competence.

Such a deliverance comes only to the few. For that huge population of schizophrenics who crowd the mental hospitals there is the shattering consciousness that they are only half alive and that for many of them lifelong reliance on reserpine is their permanent crutch. It is quite literally life-saving to the more violent, and a priceless boon to the less afflicted. Reserpine has thus all but answered the cry for relief once voiced by the frantic Macbeth:

"Canst thou not minister to the mind diseased,
    Pluck from the memory a rooted sorrow,

Raze out the written troubles of the brain;
And with some sweet oblivious antidote
Cleanse the stuffed bosom of that perilous stuff
Which weighs upon the heart?"

Wide newspaper and magazine publicity of these institutional triumphs soon led to the question of the use of reserpine in private practice. The magic words "tranquilizer" and the new wonder "tranquilizing drugs" caught the public eye like a beacon from heaven. There are millions of people who under no circumstances could be classed as schizophrenics, but still are far from completely adjusted to the stresses of modern civilization. They are not mad but distraught by a variety of external and internal tensions that leave them irritable, captious, argumentative, apprehensive and fearful of real or imaginary emergencies.

In the good old days such people would have been taught from infancy to cork all this up and "control their tantrums" —by a judicious use of the rod or gentle reasoning. Such control is no longer one of the more obvious enchantments of our younger generation and of many oldsters. They cry out now for a tranquilizer and run to the doctor or even to the drugstore—and on such a scale that millions of prescriptions are written yearly for reserpine and the synthetics that usually go with it.

The deluge of such prescriptions is so great that the sale of barbiturates has fallen off markedly. They were once the drug of choice to quiet a too rampageous patient and permit him to sleep. One reason for the popularity of reserpine is that it has no sleep-producing qualities *per se,* although it may permit an apprehensive individual to sleep normally, because of the tranquilizing effect of the drug. In other words reserpine is not a narcotic and is not, as yet, habit-forming in the sense of the compulsive use of the opium derivatives.

Of course such wholesale consumption of a tranquilizer has its detractors. One of the most distinguished of them, writing in the *Bulletin* of the New York Academy of Medicine, said, "the current trend is to escape from unpleasantness. . . . In the long run is it desirable that a population be ever free from tension? Should there be a pill for every mood or occasion?" The popular answer is an overwhelming Yes!

Quite apart from the wisdom of getting a "pill for every mood or occasion" are the possible effects of continuous use of reserpine by the general public, even under the advice of a physician. In 1956 the United States Food and Drug Administration warned doctors that the wholesale, and sometimes reckless use of reserpine might be hazardous, especially in those having stomach ulcers, a common complaint among the emotionally insecure. They list several other contingencies, the avoidance of which is obviously the responsibility of the private physician. No large doses should ever be given outside of a hospital equipped to deal with an emergency.

One of the unsolved mysteries of medicine is the usual increase in blood pressure with advancing age, and sometimes in fairly young people. Foundations have been set up to study it, but no one knows the cause of it nor is there any real cure. Merely to record the fact that arterioles shrink or get tough, and that the heart must build up enough pressure to force the blood to our uttermost extremities, tell us nothing of *why*. Least of all do they suggest a rational remedy.

It is perhaps worth repeating that those peasants in India who were being treated for mental deficiency with the root of *Rauwolfia serpentina* always showed a reduction in blood pressure. The same phenomenon was found in our mental hospitals where patients were taking the far more potent reserpine. In fact, one of the side effects of the treatment of schizophrenia with the Indian drug was so commonly a reduction in blood pressure that doctors had to watch this in case the pressure became dangerously low.

Moderately high blood pressure grows so insidiously that many people, and even their physicians, are apt to ignore it or consider it a natural concomitant of advancing age. But no one ignores the real thing evidenced by fatigue, nervousness, some palpitation, quite a bit of dizziness and a feeling of weakness. There are supposed to be about 5 per cent of the total population in this category, and without treatment their life expectancy is rather dim. Quite a few of them are overweight, and some of them suffer from impairment of kidney function, disturbance of the rhythm of the heart and may suffer "cerebral accidents."

For such patients there are innumerable drugs, but many doctors are a bit skeptical of their real value. None of them cures the basic trouble, and the side reactions of many of them make some physicians think the remedy almost as bad as the disease. This is, of course, not wholly true. Untreated cases may live for years, but most modern textbooks say that without treatment the malignant type of high blood pressure is apt to be fatal within two or three years.

Common associates of high blood pressure are nervousness, "touchiness," aggressiveness, apprehension and fear of ultimate consequences. In other words, such people much more than the general public really need a safe tranquilizer. The tremendous success of reserpine in quieting schizophrenics and its reduction of their blood pressure as a side effect of that treatment naturally suggested that the Indian drug might be useful for patients with elevated blood pressure.

It has been useful on a very wide scale. Its action is cumulative, and, under careful supervision of a physician, reserpine in from three to six weeks reduces the blood pressure and also relieves the irritability, anxiety, compulsiveness and the other symptoms that usually afflict the patient. In really serious cases it may be life-saving, and it certainly is life-prolonging. In emergencies it is often combined with other drugs that reduce blood pressure more quickly, and when the crisis is passed the patient can revert to reserpine. Some patients live for years on a maintenance dose of the drug. A few doctors have reported better results with the crude, powdered root of *Rauwolfia*, but later evidence is much in favor of reserpine.

The value of the drug in treating high blood pressure has all come within the last few years. Not many of the present generation have previously witnessed the rescue from a wild plant of India of a drug of worldwide use. In the United States the first scientific paper on reserpine in high blood pressure did not appear until 1953, and further hundreds have appeared since 1955. Some are appearing now, for the extraordinary value of *Rauwolfia* appears to make it certain that it has other uses than in treating psychotic patients and those with high blood pressure. Some doctors prescribe it for the anxiety states so common in patients with certain types of heart disease, asthma and a few other maladies. But the outstanding value of reserpine at present is for patients who are mentally deficient or have too high blood pressure.

The deserved popularity of *Rauwolfia* and its alkaloids (there are several others) has raised questions as to the quality and availability of the roots in the future. It is true that organic chemists have totally synthesized reserpine in the laboratory, in the hope that we should no longer have to rely upon wild plants. It was a scientific feat but of no practical significance, as the end-product is far too expensive to translate into bulk manufacture.

Rauwolfia serpentina is the most important source of the drug, and present supplies come from India, Pakistan, Ceylon, Burma and Thailand. This is a low shrub and the highest yield of reserpine comes from four-year-old plants, which are naturally destroyed in harvesting the root. This is best done in the autumn. At one time the Indian government put an embargo on the export of the roots, but this was lifted, and our chief source is still India.

The demand for the root became so great that there are now successful plantations of it in India, where it grows best in regions of at least 100-150 inches of rain per year and where it enjoys tropical heat. It is somewhat uncertainly propagated by seed, more reliably by root cuttings, and is 90 to 95 per cent successful if root stumps are used. These are scarcely two inches long, with a bit of the stem left on. Ultimately, as wild plants become scarce, these plantations of Indian *Rauwolfia* may be an important source of the root.

Another Indian source is the root of *Rauwolfia canescens* which appears to be *Rauwolfia tetraphylla* of tropical America. This was reputedly introduced into India, probably from Central America, in the seventeenth century. Today it has run wild over much of India and, as it contains an appreciable amount of reserpine, it is another Indian source of that drug. Some experts consider *canescens* and *tetraphylla* as distinct species.

In the former Belgian Congo and Nigeria there grows another possible source of reserpine, but it suffers from two handicaps. For one thing this *Rauwolfia vomitoria* is normally a shrub up to eighteen feet high, and harvesting the roots of such a big plant is far more difficult than with the quick-growing and much smaller *Rauwolfia serpentina*. There is also the highly unsettled state of the Congo, and even in Nigeria there may come interruption in the traffic.

The only significant American source of reserpine is *Rauwolfia tetraphylla,* harvested in Mexico, Guatemala, Costa Rica and Venezuela. It is a relatively quick-growing shrub, easily cultivated. Recently it has been taken to Queensland, Australia, where it is grown on a considerable scale. Besides the four species of *Rauwolfia* mentioned, there are at least five other species that are secondary sources of the drug. With many other species still untested, the experts not only feel safe about future supplies of reserpine but expect to find other useful products in this protean genus of plants.

As one thinks of the long and ancient history of such standard drugs as quinine, digitalis, atropine and a dozen others, the rise of reserpine has been meteoric. Like some other drugs, it had been not much more than an old wives' remedy for twenty centuries—useful, perhaps, in snakebite, in the "moon disease" and erroneously thought to cure malaria, but plentifully supplied with hocus-pocus and magic. In spite of several efforts of Indian pharmacologists to tell the story to the West, it was not until 1952, with the isolation of reserpine, that this faint Indian whisper was translated into a roar of medical approval.

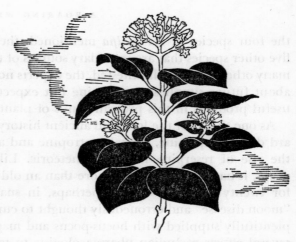

Tropical tree yielding strychnine

4. The Drug Seekers

Two criticisms are constantly hurled at the United States Food and Drug Administration. One is that they move too slowly and the other that they move too fast. They are bombarded by a deluge of often conflicting claims for new drugs, many of them tailormade in the laboratory and energetically pushed by their sponsors. Often these new proposals differ little from rival drugs that may have been on the market for years. Sometimes they are of outstanding value, and the chief function of the Administration is to tell the public if these new drugs are safe and their effectiveness up to the sometimes extravagant claims made for them by not quite disinterested manufacturers.

When Harvey Wiley finally forced, against bitter opposition, the passage of the United States Food and Drug Act in 1906, he was made the head of the Food and Drug Administration. Ever since, its main object has been to protect the public from adulterated, impure and otherwise unsafe food and drugs, no matter what greed and cupidity might claim for them. To the public nothing seemed so simple as to have new drugs submitted to the government experts and either approved or rejected within a reasonable time. In the halcyon days of 1906 that was approximately true, but today the pressure on the Administration has become almost intolerable.

On the one hand there is the urgency for speed by the pharmaceutical manufacturers who know or suspect that a rival house may be on the verge of launching a very similar drug. Against this is the pressure of the doctors who are deluged with advertisements and pestered by detail men, the latter a pharmaceutical euphemism for salesmen. Naturally the doctor hesitates to listen too closely to this clamor, even if he has the time. What physicians urgently need is up-to-the-minute and authoritative appraisal of these claimants for their patronage.

And finally there is the public, which feels helpless in the matter and must rely on the expert appraisal of these new drugs by the Food and Drug Administration, often accompanied by the dicta of the Council on Pharmacy of the American Medical Association, which also tests new drugs. All this finally filters down to the family physician.

Many millions of dollars have been at stake and still are on these decisions of the Food and Drug Administration. Legitimate profits no one objects to; the necessity for expensive research is obvious, for without it there would be no progress. But many of the public think that we pay too much for these new drugs, and the late Senator Kefauver emphatically thought so. However, since his death drug prices are not noticeably lower and the ruinous competition to produce new and high-priced drugs still goes on. Dr. L. Lasagna, a distinguished pharmacologist at Johns Hopkins University, has reflected the disillusionment of the Kefauver investigation of 1962 in a recent article in *Science* (July 14, 1964). He writes in part:

"Have drug prices been altered? Is the small drug house better or worse off than before? Are drug ads better? Has quality control improved? Are patients better protected?"

Within this welter of uncertainties stands the Food and Drug Administration. It is called "ignorant," "incompetent" and several others things by manufacturers who clamor for hasty decisions. It is blamed for "carelessness" by some doctors who remember past mistakes in releasing drugs that were of little or no value and one at least even lethal.

These seekers for new drugs are thus inevitably motivated by two rather conflicting interests. One is their genuine desire to help in the war against illness, often at a large expenditure for research and "promotion." For the latter the sums run into the millions. The other conflicting alternative is to stay in business, *i.e.*, pay regular dividends to stockholders. Their long record for this is clear evidence that they have scarcely fumbled it, and meanwhile we pay the price.

In this hectic and competitive world of pharmaceutical survival there would appear to be little room for drug seekers who, instead of hatching tailormade synthetic and high-priced drugs in a laboratory, seek elsewhere. They and the ancients, by searching the plant world for natural and healing drugs, have discovered quinine, morphine, digitalis, caffeine, cocaine, castor oil, ephedrine, reserpine and dozens of other standard drugs.

One of the largest botanical drug houses in the world has its office in New York and its collectors all over the world. To that firm is due the cultivation in the United States of the Old World foxglove, so that America not only has a source of digitalis but actually exports it. To this firm * is largely due the discovery of plant drugs, a few of them obscure but many of them standard remedies. Still more important, this company secures adequate supplies of the basic plant material, extracts the active constituents from them and thus fills an indispensable place in providing drugs of plant origin.)

The synthetic chemists are often a bit impatient of what they call empirical, old-fashioned drugs derived from plants, in spite of the number of them unavailable from any source except the plant involved. Naturally these chemists point with a good deal of justifiable pride to the synthesis of aspirin and other drugs based upon or derived indirectly from plants. One of their great triumphs was the production of wholly synthetic quinine, a wonderful chemical feat. But the synthetic product costs fantastically more than natural quinine.

(The plant world bristles with remedies, literally hundreds of them, ranging in value from old wives' "simples" to the life-saving attributes of drugs like digitalis.) Some were found by accident, others by exhaustive search in jungles, a few by observant natives and others by botanists who knew that a certain few plants of a particular family demanded a world-wide search for relatives that might yield a drug of more value. Many such searches were unsuccessful, as was the costly one in Africa for a source of cortisone.

But a few failures are swamped beneath the great number of botanical drugs that are now in general use. A few were once as common as quinine is today, but have been replaced by better species or by different extraction methods. In a few cases obsolescence has temporarily overtaken them. All of them are worth a note here, for they contain active constitu-

---

* This book has generally avoided naming any pharmaceutical manufacturers, but S. B. Penick and Company of New York, largely because of their success in discovering and supplying drugs of plant origin, makes it a pleasure to break the rule.

ents that every doctor values. Also, they help us to realize our lasting debt to the plant world, which stretches from the time of the Pharaohs to the drugstore on the corner.

A Cancer Cure?

Every pharmacologist and most botanists know that the dogbane family (Apocynaceae) contains many useful garden plants like the oleander, the beautiful allamanda, our prostrate evergreen periwinkle and several others, all of them with poisonous juice or else suspect.

Some tropical representatives of it provide deadly arrow poisons which have yielded valuable drugs such as ouabain and strophanthin, which are discussed in the chapter headed "The Helpful Poisoners."

So notorious is the family for containing poisonous or suspect juices that the pharmacologists have explored many of the thousand different species in it. As late as 1961, Drs. R. F. Raffauf and M. B. Flagler issued an account of them entitled, "Alkaloids of the Apocynaceae." In that scholarly paper they list nearly two hundred alkaloids found in various plants in that family, several of them yielding such valuable drugs as reserpine, strophanthin, ouabain and a few others.

Still more recently have come many papers on the so-called Madagascar periwinkle, which is first cousin to our common, evergreen periwinkle, sometimes called creeping myrtle and familiar to every gardener as a fine, prostrate ground cover. The Madagascar periwinkle, however, is an erect perennial, eighteen to twenty-four inches high, with white flowers with a pink "eye" or else all pink and usually blooming all summer. It is technically called *Vinca rosea,* but some call it *Catharanthus roseus.* It is a tropical plant, will not stand northern winters, and is grown as a tender annual, which must be planted every year. It, too, belongs to the Apocynaceae.

Vinca rosea has recently generated a great amount of interest, for it contains about a dozen reputedly different alkaloids, some of which have been tested upon experimental animals. The results in animals that had been inoculated with a known strain of cancer were so encouraging that it led to much experimentation on different forms of cancer with the therapeutically promising alkaloids of the plant.

These are obtained from the juice of the leaves, and as it has only a few of these, the supplies seemed precarious and were, of course, expensive. In the tropics and perhaps in the Deep South of the United States the plant is a little taller, more vigorous and apparently contains more alkaloids than the annual garden plant of the north. But the unhappy truth is that *Vinca rosea* contains only minute amounts of significant alkaloids. Some estimates are as low as 0.00025 per cent. That is so microscopic a yield that unless large-scale production of the plant is assured, its place in anti-cancer therapy seems still a bit nebulous.

However, its success in arresting cancerous growth in experimental animals naturally suggested its trial on human beings. One of its possible uses was in the treatment of Hodgkin's disease, a progressive, inevitably fatal disease, thought by some experts to be allied to or a form of cancer. The reports were favorable, although no one knows yet whether the disease was "cured" or not, for the progress of the disease is slow, and ultimate death may not come for years. All of the cases of Hodgkin's disease treated with the alkaloids of *Vinca rosea* have been since 1961, so that it is hazardous to make extravagant claims of a "cure."

Another disease upon which it has been tried is leukemia, also ultimately fatal, and often attacking young people. This is a "type of cancer of the blood-forming organs," heretofore considered incurable, but often treated with palliatives that may postpone the fatal outcome. The use of the alkaloids of

Vinca rosea on children with leukemia appears to have some value, but as the progress of that disease is very slow, and the treatment started around 1961, the ultimate results are still inconclusive. Usually leukemia patients, unless they have a relatively rapid form of it, live from three to four years after it is diagnosed, and some much longer. In other words, it is still much too early to announce a "cure" of leukemia or of any other form of cancer.

Much nonsensical newspaper publicity has been released about the Madagascar periwinkle to the consternation of careful physicians and the large battery of chemists and pharmacologists involved in the study of this promising plant of the Apocynaceae. The tragedy of such irresponsible publicity is that sufferers and their families are buoyed up by it, naturally thinking that a cure for their affliction is readily available. Responsible scientists know better. They know that *Vinca rosea* has opened up amazing avenues of research, which are being investigated by innumerable experts, few or perhaps none of whom would claim that the Madagascar periwinkle is a cure for cancer.

Rat Poison and a Heart Remedy

All along the Mediterranean there grow a series of bulbous plants known as squill which are closely related to our beautiful garden *Scilla*. One of them, the red squill from the African coast, contains such a virulent poison in its bulb that it is a common ingredient of the usual rat poisons. Its close relative, the so-called sea onion, grows along the sandy dunes and beaches from Spain to Greece and has been famous for over 3,500 years as a cure for dropsy. It is definitely mentioned in the *Ebers Papyrus,* found at Luxor, Egypt, which is known to have been written about 1500 B.C.

Unlike our garden scillas, the sea onion has a very large

bulb, from seven to twelve inches in diameter at maturity, but usually harvested when about half that size. It has pointed leaves twelve to eighteen inches long, and sends up a flowering stalk one to three feet high, crowned by a long cluster of small, whitish flowers. Unlike many bulbous plants, the better part of the bulb is above the surface, so that the sea onion appears as if only half planted. The plant is known to botanists and pharmacologists as *Urginea maritima* and belongs to the lily family.

What drug seeker first discovered its properties we shall never know. It was sufficiently familiar at the time of the *Ebers Papyrus* to suggest it must have been known considerably before 1500 B.C., as it is mentioned among a dozen other drugs, many of which are in use today and have become such standard remedies that they are included in the *United States Pharmacopœia*. The sea onion is not listed, but until the classic work of Dr. Withering on digitalis it was for three thousand years a widely used heart remedy.

In the first century of our era the Romans were using the sea onion to reduce dropsy and as what they called a "heart tonic." No one suspected then that dropsy was not itself a disease but usually a manifestation of a fundamental heart irregularity. While the sea onion did rid the body of accumulated liquid (a diuretic), it did so, unknown to the Romans, by its action on the heart, which is very like the action of digitalis. Hence those Romans who called it a "heart tonic" were nearly eighteen hundred years ahead of the medical profession in England, who never connected digitalis or the sea onion with their ability to control what is now called the failing heart or congestive heart failure. This was not known until early in the nineteenth century.

The active principle in the sea onion (*Urginea maritima*) is found only in its bulb, and in but a part of it. The bulb, which when fresh may weigh four to seven pounds, has an exterior, parchment-like outer coating much like a garden onion. Inside there are innumerable scale-like segments of the bulb which contain a sticky juice that is so irritant that it will raise blisters on the hands. The remarkable feature of the bulb is that the active principle is found only in a layer of the inner scales. The outer scales and the central ones are quite inert. Few vagaries of nature are so selective as this. How an early Egyptian drug seeker ever hit upon such a well-hidden secret must always remain a mystery.

But there is no mystery about its wide use for centuries before the discovery of digitalis. Its action is so close to digitalis that its use was perfectly understandable before the epoch-making studies on the foxglove by Dr. Withering in Birmingham about the time of the United States Revolution. All European doctors were constantly on the alert to find drugs that had a digitalis-like action on the heart, and the sea onion was one of the oldest.

Its popularity has now waned, as have several other substitutes for digitalis, like the one used by the Russians for centuries. They extracted from the rootstocks of the common lily-of-the-valley (*Convallaria majalis*) an active principle with digitalis-like action on the heart but inferior to it. Another was found in the seeds of the yellow oleander (*Thevetia nerifolia*) which was named for the Franciscan monk Andre Thevet, who went from France to Rio de Janeiro in 1556 and first brought tobacco to Europe. But this tropical American plant is also inferior to digitalis and is now known mostly as a scientific curiosity.

The hunt for heart remedies has not waned, for the synthetic chemists are actively engaged in finding what they hope will be better drugs than existing ones. But besides the two mentioned above, the plant drug seekers have not been idle. One of their "finds" is a very ancient one known to the Chinese for centuries. They used to tip their arrows with a poison derived from the root of the common garden monkshood (*Aconitum napellus*), a plant so dangerous that Shakespeare, in *King Henry IV*, likens its strength to that of gunpowder. And the "dram of poison" which Romeo craved was none other than aconite. Its use in medicine today is properly much restricted, although it does slow the heart rate and reduce blood pressure. However, the difference between a toxic (often deadly) and therapeutic dose is much too close for safety.

Another candidate from the wild is the common false hellebore (*Veratrum viride*), which is violently poisonous. It grows in swampy woods throughout the eastern United States, and from its roots is extracted an active principle once used to reduce the heart rate and induce a fall in blood pressure. But one modern authority has written that as of today, "The drug is dangerous and should not be used clinically."

While the sea onion has also waned as a heart remedy, it is still described in the latest edition of the *United States Dispensatory* (1960), where it is specified that the drug must be derived from "the cut and dried fleshy inner scales of the bulb of the white variety of *Urginea maritima*, . . . or of *Urginea indica*." The latter is found along the seashores of India and is less used than the European sea onion.

The *Dispensatory* does not include the so-called red squill, although it is also called *Urginea maritima*, contains the same useful active principle as the sea onion, and is considered a mere variety of it by most botanists. But it is excluded from medical use because it also contains a violently poisonous principle, deadly to rats, mice and guinea pigs. That is why it is used in many commercial rat poisons, but never as an ingredient of heart remedies.

Poisonous Flowers

When the French government put a stop to the manufacture of absinthe, they well knew that the oil extracted from the flowers of the ashy-leaved wormwood had disastrous effects upon the boulevardiers addicted to that liqueur. So poisonous is that enticingly aromatic oil that habitués became stuporous and many ended up in convulsions.

Wormwood and its relatives belong to a group of plants known as *Artemisia,* a huge genus scattered all over the world, common examples being tarragon and the sagebrush of the drier parts of western United States. The latter is a shrub, but most of them are herbs, nearly all being aromatic and some, like tarragon, having a bitter principle in their leaves.

Artemisia belongs to the daisy family (Compositae), a few of which have the unusual attribute of secreting an oil in their flowers which has been captured for medicinal use for centuries. Another plant in this protean family whose flowers are harvested on a huge scale is a *Chrysanthemum,* the only source of pyrethrum powder so widely used as a relatively safe insecticide, for it is only lethal to cold-blooded animals. It is not the pyrethrum of our gardens, and is grown mostly in Kenya and Ecuador.

The fact that the flowers of a few plants in the Compositae family yield an oil poisonous to insects has been elaborated on a great scale in warm regions, where intestinal worms flourish among millions of people. Tapeworms and roundworms are common examples; hence possibly the coining of the term *wormwood* for several species of *Artemisia,* some of which are almost a specific for intestinal worms.

One of the most used is *Artemisia Cinna,* a small-leaved, woody perennial from Persia and Turkestan, growing about two feet high and producing a tremendous number of yellow flower heads that are scarcely one-tenth of an inch in diameter. Closely related and very similar is *Artemisia maritima* which grows on sandy beaches from England to China. A few other species of *Artemisia,* some of them American, also bear small flower heads that yield an oil of value, because, like the two chief sources, that oil is lethal only to insects.

Many years ago, when these species of *Artemisia* were being studied in the laboratories of Europe, the plants were usually called santonica and the active principle in the oil was, and still is, called *Santonin.* For centuries before these terms were coined, people who lived in regions where intestinal worms were rife had been using decoctions of the flower heads of these artemisias to rid them of the parasites.

Perhaps they did not know that santonin, in therapeutic doses, has little or no effect upon the human body and hence is perhaps not entitled to the distinction of being a healing drug at all. But its action on the intestinal worms is dramatic. Left to their own devices, these creatures would mature enough to puncture the wall of the intestine with highly unpleasant and ultimately fatal results.

It is precisely at this juncture that santonin does its remarkable job of causing spasmodic contractions of the muscle fibers of the worm so that it no longer has the power of purposeful movements. The paralyzed worms are then purged with an active cathartic. It is thus not too fanciful to call santonin an intestinal insecticide, for while it does not kill the worms, it enables a cathartic to flush them out before they have done any damage.

Santonin has some undesirable side actions and in overdoses is definitely dangerous to man. Because of this there are now several synthetic substitutes for it, but *Artemisia Cinna* and *Artemisia maritima* are still cultivated on a considerable scale in Russia, Pakistan and Persia. For some inscrutable reason the tiny flowers of these plants are commonly called in the trade Levant wormseed, a singularly inappropriate name, for no seeds are used, only the highly poisonous and valuable flowers. It is not a remedy for amoebic dysentery, which is found later in this chapter.

Still another plant used for intestinal worms is the common weedy American wormseed (*Chenopodium ambrosioides anthelminticum*), the latter name meaning a destroyer of intestinal worms. Its foliage and seeds yield chenopodium oil, thought by some to be superior to santonin, but often replaced by synthetic drugs. It is a rank-smelling herb, originally native in tropical America, but now a pestiferous weed in gardens.

That fatal and perfidious drug
Built in the eclipse and rigged with curses dark.
                                                            —*Lycidas.*

In England about the time that John Milton was writing his beautiful pastoral poem on Lycidas, in November 1637, there arrived in London some poisonous seeds so dangerous that they were used only as an ingredient of rat poison. No one suspected then that a proper dilution of an extract of these seeds would ever become a welcome addition to tonic mixtures that today are often mixed with wine and iron. Those seeds were the source of strychnine.

Its origin is a tree of moderate size, a native of India, Ceylon and regions to the east. It belongs to a family of plants known as the Loganiaceae, which also yield one of the ingredients of the South American curare. This Indian plant is an evergreen tree scarcely forty feet high, with terminal clusters of small greenish flowers, followed by an orange-shaped fruit about two inches in diameter, and with a hard rind. Inside is a fleshy pulp embedded in which are several flattish seeds. The plant was properly named by Linnaeus as

Strychnos Nux-vomica, but the father of botany perpetuated an error in the latter name, for the seeds have no action either to promote or retard vomiting.

That error has persisted to this day, for the seeds are still known by pharmacologists and in the trade as *Nux-vomica.* No wonder it fooled Milton, as it certainly deceived Linnaeus. But far more important than poetic and botanical errors is the fact that Nux-vomica seeds contain two of the bitterest and certainly most dangerous alkaloids. Ever since their discovery, they have been known as brucine and strychnine. The latter is so bitter that it can be tasted in dilutions of four hundred thousand parts of water to a single part of strychnine.

Most physicians and nearly all competent pharmacologists sniff at the term "tonic," but the public pays little attention to them. Ever since the middle part of the nineteenth century there have been many popular tonics that contain quinine, iron and a minute amount of strychnine. So true is this that the United States imports large amounts of Nux-vomica seeds. Most laymen insist that such tonics make them feel better, promote the secretion of digestive fluids, increase appetite and are hence useful and valuable preparations. One of the leading pharmacological textbooks merely echoes the experts when it states that such tonics are "an irrational and complex mixture."—(Goodman and Gilman: *The Pharmacological Basis of Therapeutics*)

However, strychnine as a drug, in spite of its dangers, has a place in medical emergencies. It is a curious fact that all the New World plants of *Strychnos* have a relaxing effect upon the nervous system and the muscles controlled by it, which makes curare so valuable in surgery. But the Old World species of *Strychnos* have exactly an opposite effect. In other words, strychnine is very different in its action from curare, in spite of the fact that they are derived from closely related plants.

Strychnine is an extremely dangerous drug. Even a small overdose produces violent convulsions, as it acts directly on the spinal cord. The victim's head and feet are the only part of his body to touch the ground during a seizure, and his face is rigid in a hideous grin. The convulsion may last a minute or two and be repeated within ten to fifteen minutes, and the patient is completely conscious during the ordeal. Without treatment a fatal outcome is usual.

Of what possible use is such a potentially lethal drug? In therapeutic doses it greatly increases mental and muscular activity, even approaching a condition where twitching of the muscles is a sign that the drug is nearing toxic levels. It once had a wide use to increase circulation of the blood and was assumed to have some beneficial effect upon the heart. Both assumptions are now much doubted by the experts, for the danger of promoting convulsions is an ever-present hazard.

Perhaps its chief use today is in the treatment of patients who are stuporous from ingestion of too much morphine, alcohol (delirium tremens) and other depressant drugs. Such patients can stand considerably larger doses than normal, and the exciting effects in stimulating the nervous system and muscles make strychnine a useful, but still a hazardous drug. In spite of this it has been synthesized and ultimately we may not have to import Nux-vomica seeds.

The King and a Quack

Louis XIV, with all his splendor, intelligence and corruption was singularly naïve about medical quacks. In the chapter on malaria and quinine there is an account of the kingly innocence in believing the greatest quack the world has ever known. Not to be outdone by the English Robert Talbor, a

Dutch quack reached Paris and promptly changed his name from Schweitzer to Jean Adrien Helvetius. This ingenious entrepreneur was soon hawking the "remedies" of his Dutch father, also a quack, and doing well at it.

In one of his visits to patients Helvetius got hold of a new remedy from Brazil said to be good for dysentery and found it remarkably effective. Without divulging its constituents, he soon placarded the streets of Paris with notices of his remedy, so that in 1688 he was by way of becoming famous.

Jean Baptiste Colbert, who was credited with practically running France for the King, told Louis XIV, just then enmeshed with one of his mistresses, about the remarkable "cures" that Helvetius was making all over Paris. If the King had one soft spot it was for his son the Dauphin, often ill with dysentery. Louis insisted that Helvetius be summoned to the palace, and he promptly cured the Dauphin. The King immediately started proceedings, through his confessor Père de la Chaise, to buy the formula from the Dutch quack.

Helvetius sold the formula for a thousand louis d'or and ultimately became the grandfather of Claude Adrien Helvetius, the famous French philosopher and poet. The quack soon was appointed as Inspector General of French Hospitals and became physician to the Duke of Orleans.

Under these somewhat cloudy auspices was born the use of *ipecac* in European medicine. If Helvetius was not a drug seeker, he found or at least publicized in 1688 a drug that has since gone around the world. It was true that it came from South America, but at that time no European physician had ever heard of it.

But the Indians in Brazil were not so ignorant. For many years before this, and probably for centuries, they had been using a decoction of the roots of a medium-sized shrub for the cure of amebic dysentery. This is primarily a disease of tropical and warm regions, but is sometimes found in the north,

spread by the unwashed and infected hands of kitchen workers who handle food. It can be contracted only from ingestion
of food or water infected by a microscopic amoeba. Perhaps
50 per cent of tropical people are so infected, often several
times. Untreated cases average 20 to 40 per cent of deaths,
while properly treated cases rarely go over 5 per cent of
deaths.

The original Brazilian treatment (and ours today) was
based on the fact that the jungle shrub, known as *Cephaelis
Ipecacuanha,* contains an alkaloid, emetine, which is *the*
remedy for amebic dysentery. The Indians, of course, knew
nothing of emetine, an alkaloid first isolated in pure form in
1829. It was called emetine because in certain doses it pro-
vokes vomiting, and was once widely used for just that property when it was obligatory quickly to evacuate poisons from
the stomach. Other methods have supplanted ipecac in these
emergencies.

But in amebic dysentery it is still so widely used that this
Brazilian shrub is cultivated on a considerable scale in India
and Malaya, where amebic dysentery is very prevalent. While
it is true that emetine is the drug of choice for the distressing
symptoms of the disease, it does not kill all the parasites, so
that after making the patient apparently "cured," he may still
be harboring infective material and become a carrier. Such
people are a public health menace and for this stage of the
disease, which may show no outward symptoms, there are
several synthetic drugs of great value. So dangerous are these
carriers and so common is the parasite in many tropical soils
that careful travelers avoid fresh vegetables grown in the
tropics unless they are boiled or otherwise sterilized.

Often, in severe cases, the disease may cause abscesses of the
liver, lung or brain. Such cases are usually treated only with
emetine at first, later, if need be, by one of the synthetics.
This shrub of tropical America thus has a definite and re-

stricted, but also invaluable use in amebic dysentery, quite apart from its ability to promote both vomiting and diarrhea when these are essential.

The plant yielding ipecac and its active principle emetine is a rather inconspicuous, sprawling shrub, belonging to the same family (Rubiaceae) that yields coffee and quinine and includes the familiar roadside United States shrub known as buttonbush (*Cephalanthus occidentalis*). The ipecac plant is scarcely over eighteen inches high, bears opposite, evergreen leaves and small white flowers. The root, which is the only part of any medicinal value, is branching, and contains the most emetine when three or four years old. It grows only in hot, steamy, shady jungles and is largely harvested by native labor. In India and Malaya its culture is restricted to similar climates.

Ipecac has a few minor uses, none of them medically important, but the drug might have been buried in obscurity for years if it had not been uncovered by Louis XIV. That monarch could scarcely be called a drug seeker, for he was busy seeking mistresses by whom he produced a large crop of illegitimate children. But drug seekers should not deny this illustrious king the honor of rescuing from a Dutch quack the Brazilian ipecac.

Friar's Balsam and the Croup

A lovely smelling balsamic resin usually called friar's balsam was once so widely treasured that it was much imitated and had a variety of other names like Jesuit's drops, St. Victor's balsam and Jerusalem balsam. All of these were taken internally for a miserable condition of the chest which made coughs hard, dry and what the doctors call unproductive.

The resin itself was not swallowed, but a tincture of it was so effective in generating a productive cough that the world

was scoured to find the proper ingredients for it. In all prob-
ability a Portuguese merchant invented the first of these
remedies, but his base was the Balsam of Peru. A little later
friar's balsam contained a very different ingredient coming
from the East Indies and Siam.

It is impossible today to unravel the controversy that raged
in England over the constituents and the relative value of the
imitations of friar's balsam, but it lasted well over a hundred
years. The remedy was so popular that much money was involved, but a formula for it was finally admitted into medical
literature when published by the authorities of the Medicine
Stamp Act, on June 13, 1777.

This showed that the chief and most effective ingredient of
all these remedies was a highly aromatic balsamic resin obtained from an East Indian tree commonly called storax, but
known to the botanists as *Styrax*. That plants of this genus
had valuable constituents had been known for centuries, for
in the thirtieth chapter of Exodus and the twenty-fourth
chapter of Ecclesiasticus the tree is mentioned as the source of
another medicine derived from *Styrax officinalis*. This is a
medium-sized tree or shrub which grows in Palestine and
yields an aromatic gum resin.

The balsamic resin in friar's balsam is very different from
that found in Israel, for it comes from only two places:
Sumatra and Siam. The best known is from Sumatra and is
yielded by a large, quick-growing tree called *Styrax Benzoin*,
which also grows in Java and Borneo. The closely related
Siamese tree (*Styrax benzoides* or *Styrax tonkinensis*) grows
in a very limited area in the province of Luang Probang
along the Mekong River.

The only part of these trees of any medicinal value is the
resin exuded from cuts made in the bark. These are triangu-
lar incisions from which oozes the sap, which, upon coagulation, is Sumatra benzoin. Similar cuts in the Siamese trees

yield Siam benzoin. These aromatic gum resins are so nearly alike that they are both admitted into the *United States Pharmacopœia* as Benzoin, known to every mother with croupy infants.

For centuries before benzoin reached Europe, the Hindus used it as a sort of incense in their temples because of its delicious vanilla-like odor. Today the pharmacologists who may be just as fond of its odor have extracted from the gum the active constituent of benzoin, usually called benzoic acid. In modern medicine crude benzoin is practically never taken internally, as it is rather bitter and may cause complications. Instead we use tincture of benzoin made by mixing benzoin with alcohol and one or two other ingredients.

This was the basis of friar's balsam, a completely obsolete name for a mixture, the main constituent of which was a tincture of benzoin. But that tincture is far from obsolete today and is usually called simply benzoin. It enters into a few remedies for coughs, bronchitis, etc., for which it is taken internally. It is an expectorant, loosens up unproductive coughs and is still favored by some physicians.

By far the most widely acclaimed virtue of benzoin is the nearly universal use of it by frightened and harassed mothers whose children have croup. That disease is considered by some as a medical nuisance, but any mother whose infant has a racking, unproductive cough knows better. Nothing is more painful than to see a feverish child trying desperately to raise apparently immovable sputum from its bronchial tubes. Technically, croup is called acute obstructive laryngitis, and fortunately it is very rarely fatal and only if the obstructive material cannot be coughed up.

In such emergencies the gum resin of these Asiatic trees has been used ever since the tincture of benzoin became available. A single teaspoonful of the tincture is put in a pint of water which is then raised to the boiling point. Under a tent, often made from a sheet, the vapor or near-steam of the mixture is inhaled by the child. The theory behind this is that benzoin is an expectorant and loosens up an unproductive cough, and so should the steam from a kettle of water and tincture of benzoin. It usually does, and because of that, the mixture has wide and grateful usage.

None of the expert pharmacologists agree about the cure. They say that it is the steam that loosens up the cough and sometimes saves the child's life, not the benzoin. That would remove benzoin from the list of useful remedies, deny it a place in the *United States Pharmacopœie* and deprive us of an enticingly aromatic remedy which may well survive the strictures of the experts.

The Frisky Goats and That Second Cup of Coffee

Somewhere about A.D. 900 an Abyssinian goatherd was astonished to see his animals become abnormally frisky. He wondered why. These creatures are scarcely epicurean about their diet, and were found to be eating the bright red fruit of a native shrub or small tree. Unknown to the herder, these frisky goats pointed the way to the most widely used beverage on earth.

Such is the legendary "history" of the discovery of coffee. It is no doubt false, but what is certainly true is that coffee was taken from Ethiopia to Arabia in the tenth century and cultivated in the Yemen, the only part of that desert country fit for it. It is a tropical crop, but needs some coolness and plenty of moisture. In the mountains of Yemen it found a salubrious substitute for the conditions in its homeland.

Soon after its introduction into Arabia, it was written up by that master Arabian physician, Avicenna, whose medical books were standard for five hundred years after they appeared. It is unquestionable that Avicenna gave to the Western world the first written account of coffee late in the tenth century. But Europe paid no attention to him and the first coffee to reach England did not get to London until Sir Anthony Sherley brought it there from Persia in 1601.

But in 1554 the first coffeehouse in the world was opened at Constantinople, and by 1625 there were thousands of coffeehouses flourishing in Cairo, in one of which someone had the wit to add sugar to the beverage.* From that has come the worldwide use of the coffee berries found in the red fruit that is supposed to have attracted the Abyssinian goats.

Not until 1753 was the coffee plant named *Coffea arabica,* the latter specific name being an error of Linnaeus, who assumed that Arabia was its native home. Perhaps the father of botany knew that the finest coffee in the world then came from Mocha, a town in the Yemen. Today Brazil produces two thirds of the world crop, which is measured in millions of bags of one hundred thirty-two pounds each.

Unknown to Avicenna and to the millions of coffee drinkers all over Europe was the fact that they drank it for its content of caffeine, an alkaloid that remained hidden until 1821. In that year a French chemist, Pierre Jean Robiquet, had an idea that because the coffee plant and the tree that yields quinine both belonged to the madder family (Rubiaceae), he might find quinine in the coffee plant. He found no quinine, but was the first to isolate caffeine as a result of his quinine quest.

Several hundred years before this, Avicenna was convinced that coffee was a useful stimulant, and he sometimes needed it. It has been written of this prince of Arabian physicians by Dr. A. C. Wooton that,

* The history of coffee as a beverage and its effects on the life of London and New York will be found in the writer's *Narcotics: Nature's Dangerous Gifts,* Dell Publishing Co., New York, 1963.

All his philosophy failed to make him moral, and all his knowledge of medicine left him unable to take care of his own health.

He died in 1037, and to him we owe the concept that caffeine is a stimulant, although he knew nothing of the existence of that alkaloid. One of the first things noticed about coffee was its great ability to keep people awake. So famous was this attribute that Christian monks were urged to drink it to keep alert during midnight vigils. And the interminable Moslem services, before the advent of coffee, often led sleepy-eyed worshipers to doze off, so that Mohammedans as well as Christians welcomed coffee as an eye opener. Some of us today shun coffee in the evening, because we know or think it will do the same for us.

The ordinary cup of coffee, of the usual breakfast strength, contains about one and a half grains of caffeine (100 mg.). That "second cup of coffee" hence means just about three grains of caffeine at one sitting. Its effects upon the nervous system, the increased capacity for thinking, its stimulating effects on circulation and muscular activity, not to speak of its sparking greater fluency—these are attributes of the beverage that few will give up. If it has any dangers, most of us, in ordinary doses, are inclined to ignore them. But there is no doubt that excessive intake of caffeine at one time, say up to seven or eight grains (*i.e.*, 5 or 6 cups), has harmful effects such as restlessness, nervous irritability, insomnia, muscular tremor and a few other sequelae. The lethal dose in man is unknown, for there are no records of it. Experimental animals die in convulsions after overdoses and from such studies it is assumed that a fatal dose of caffeine in man may be about 150 grains (*i.e.*, one-half ounce). That would mean about one hundred cups of coffee!

Caffeine is thus a potent alkaloid, much used in the last war to keep aviators awake. But it is of secondary medical importance today, although it has some useful attributes. It stimulates blood flow and the heart rate, as well as the central nervous system. For this reason caffeine was, and still is to many physicians, the ideal drug to give those patients who are practically comatose from poisoning by the barbiturates, morphine, alcohol, etc. It also has considerable use to promote the elimination of too much body fluid (*i.e.,* edema). It also has rather wide use among the laity in some of the so-called "pep" pills, especially among students and writers. Such caffeine pills stimulate mental activity, although there must be ultimately a letdown, as an aftermath of nearly all stimulants.

Coffee is too expensive to be a profitable source of caffeine, although it contains about one and one-half per cent of that alkaloid. The kola nut of Africa and guaraná from Brazil both contain far more caffeine than coffee. But both are also too expensive to make caffeine extraction profitable. This impasse was finally solved by the organic chemists.

In the harvesting and preparation of tea there is a tremendous wastage of broken or powdered tea leaves unfit for the market. The alkaloid in tea, known as theine, is so similar to caffeine that some chemists insist they are practically identical. And many laymen know to their cost how a few cups of tea will banish sleep for hours. At any rate, the conversion of theine into caffeine is no problem.

Hence, today, the cheapest and only large-scale source of caffeine is the sweepings of the tea refuse in India, Java, Formosa and Japan. Most of it is shipped to Europe and a good deal of it converted from theine to caffeine in Holland.

While caffeine may be of minor medical importance, no one can ignore the greatest source of it in coffee. We drink that second cup with fervor, and some do even more. Perhaps they remember Pope's "Rape of the Lock," with its reference to

> Coffee, which makes the politician wise,
> And see through all things with his half-shut eyes.

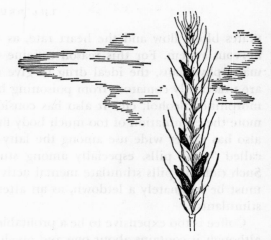

Ergot: a blessing and a scourge

5. Doctor Hosack and St. Anthony's Fire

DR. DAVID HOSACK (1769-1835) ought to be known to every New Yorker, for he gave to Columbia University the land upon which he had started the first botanic garden in the city. It was a considerable tract, still owned by Columbia and now covered with the buildings of Rockefeller Center. Hosack was made professor of botany at Columbia in 1795 and soon after the professor "of the theory and practice of physic," in what is now the College of Physicians and Surgeons of Columbia University.

Perhaps his interest in botany and medicine sparked an activity better known to the medical profession than the gift of his botanic garden to Columbia. Much involved in trying to make childbirth safer and with less blood loss, he published a paper in 1824 warning that the number of stillborn babies had increased so alarmingly that he urged the Medical Society of New York to do something about it. Hosack's strictures were all aimed at a drug that had recently been introduced into the United States, although its history goes back to the ancients.

Its use started in New York in 1807 with the publication in the *Medical Repository* of a paper entitled, "Account of the Pulvis Parturiens, a remedy for quickening childbirth," written by Dr. John Stearns, the first president of the New York Academy of Medicine. His Latin name for the drug could be roughly translated as "The Powder to Promote Childbirth." This was *ergot*, then practically unknown to American medicine but familiar to every European midwife, and the cause of a dreadful disease known as St. Anthony's Fire.

All over the world farmers are plagued by various smuts and rusts that attack grain crops. In the United States these microscopic pests do damage measured in the millions of dollars. Most of them are caused by minute fungus spores which flourish when the weather is warm and moist. Wheat rust is a common example, and the ergot on rye is by far the most notorious. Ergot can grow on other grasses besides rye, but the *United States Pharmacopœie* says that medicinal ergot must come from diseased rye plants.

The production of ergot on rye is a fantastically complex and apparently fortuitous operation. The fungus that causes it is known as *Claviceps purpurea*, and its spores are carried by the wind or insects to the fruiting spike of rye. The spores originate from a dormant, winter stage of the fungus found in the soil, which, as the growing season matures, releases these microscopic messengers of infection. The spores attack the ovaries of the maturing spikelet of rye and completely destroy them. This is followed, not by a normal grain of rye, but by a small, spur-like blackish growth, called by the French *argot* (a spur), hence our term *ergot*.

The mature ergot, which may attack several ovaries in the

same spike, is a slightly furrowed structure, pointed at both ends and varying from one-half to two inches in length, slightly curved, black or brownish on the outside, but white on the inside when fresh. It contains an amazing battery of alkaloids, and provides for its perpetuation by depositing on the ground enough of the still living organisms to winter over and begin the dread cycle the following spring.

Wherever rye can be grown, ergot is possible. For a very long time it was considered as merely a disease, and infected plants were destroyed by worried farmers. Today they are cultivating rye and deliberately inoculating the crop with the spores of ergot, so great is the demand for that drug. This is done under controlled conditions, to prevent the infection from spreading to other grains, for it must never be forgotten that ergot is a pestiferous disease of grasses and can do much damage.

Ever since the time of the Romans, failure of grain crops has been periodic, and famine or near-famine an ever-present hazard to the peasants of Europe. At such times the food scarcity forced the use of ergot-infested rye. The effects have been almost beyond belief. During the Middle Ages, and long after, there are records of a horrible disease caused by the ingestion of even small amounts of this ergot-infested rye in the tenth, eleventh and twelfth centuries. Spontaneous abortion by pregnant women was the least of the troubles. Ergot tends to contract the blood vessels, thus cutting off normal blood flow to the extremities, which usually become discolored and ultimately gangrenous. Arms, hands, legs and feet become black and, without any blood loss or appreciable pain, fall off, much as a leaf falls in autumn.

Thousands of people were killed by what they called St. Anthony's Fire, because the peasants believed that a pilgrimage to that shrine might cure the loathsome disease. It often did, probably by a change of diet *en route* to Egypt.

With a better distribution of food and more careful milling of rye flour, St. Anthony's Fire is practically unknown today. But even as late as 1926, Russia had an outbreak in the Ukraine, and smaller eruptions occurred in Belgium and Ireland. These happened when less than 1 per cent of the rye was impregnated with ergot, so poisonous is this infection. Sporadic cases still crop up, as those that occurred in the early part of this century in New York, Ohio, and Kansas.

Ergotism, besides causing the loss of limbs following the gangrene brought on by cutting off the blood flow, also produces undesirable effects upon the central nervous system, leading in overdoses to confusion, drowsiness, pain on one side of the head and in one eye, and in advanced cases ending in convulsions and death.

Not all cases of St. Anthony's Fire are so drastic, and the amount of involvement usually depends upon the amount of infected bread that has been eaten. But that ergot is dangerous is amply verified, even as far back as 600 B.C. An Assyrian tablet of that date warns against "a noxious pustule in the ear of grain." And two hundred years later the Parsees wrote: "Among the evil things created . . . are noxious grasses that cause pregnant women to drop the womb and die in childbed."

St. Anthony's Fire, also called Holy Fire, at first causes a burning or tingling in the extremities, long before its more drastic effects are evident. In spite of these dangers the midwives of Europe used ergot in childbirth centuries before the medical profession ever heard of it. The midwives were using the crude drug to promote and strengthen uterine contractions, for no one then knew what were its active constituents, and even the concept of an alkaloid was far in the future. Without that knowledge, and avoiding its hazards, these midwives pointed the way to the worldwide use of the derivatives of ergot, now a standard drug in obstetrics. Scarcely any doctor today uses the crude drug, for its amazing collection of alkaloids are much safer and more effective.

The use of ergot in obstetrics was known to the midwives long before the cause of St. Anthony's Fire was also found to be an attribute of the diseased kernels of rye. No one knew the mechanism of its action for centuries after its habitual use in obstetrics. And the determination of the fact that, in improper doses, it causes what we now called ergotism, or St. Anthony's Fire, was not discovered until long after its obstetrical use.

The first alkaloid of ergot was not isolated until 1875, and it proved to be completely inert. That failure sparked further research, for it was obvious that such a powerful drug as ergot must contain at least one potent alkaloid. But not until 1906 was the first medically significant alkaloid obtained and called *ergotoxine.* In 1920, two more alkaloids of ergot were isolated and called *ergotamine* and *ergotaminine.*

Since then nearly a dozen other alkaloids have been found in ergot, so that the confusion of the layman would be complete if the whole matter had not simmered down to the extraordinary effects of just a few of them, notably in obstetrics and in correcting migraine headaches.

In obstetrics still another alkaloid of ergot, known as *ergonovine,* has come to be widely used. It was not isolated until 1935 and has a direct, swift and powerful action upon contractions of the pregnant uterus. Like ergot itself, and all its alkaloids, ergonovine is never used in the first or second stages of labor, for at that time it may well cause the death of the baby and not infrequently of the mother.

But in the third stage of labor ergonovine has dramatic and very favorable effects. Within minutes of an injection of the drug, uterine contractions are strengthened and the baby is born. The necessary sequelae are so helped that some doctors withhold the drug until after the infant is born. Dr. Hosack, in his paper of 1824, warned that ergot was even best used "only to control postpartum hemorrhage." He, of course, was talking only about crude ergot. In other words this wise old physician, more than a century ago, pointed out the proper use of the drug and deplored its improper use, which had caused so many stillborn accidents in New York.

Ergonovine is so powerful that doses of it vary from 1/120 to 1/300 of a grain, an almost microscopic dose. It has the extraordinarily selective action of causing strong contractions of the pregnant uterus, with little or no serious side effects. Its effects on the non-pregnant uterus are negligible. Naturally its efficacy in helping to evacuate the contents of the pregnant uterus has been seized upon by terrified girls who, failing a husband, want a quick release from their predicament. Such abortions are illegal, very dangerous, and a few of them end fatally.

The early accounts of St. Anthony's Fire all stress the fact that ergot had marked effects on the central nervous system causing, besides the rotting of limbs, an obvious alteration in mental adjustments. The discovery of the alkaloids of ergot and the certainty of being able to prescribe a measured dose of the alkaloid, even if very small, opened up a new line of research for neurologists and psychiatrists.

One of the most distressing complaints that afflict us is migraine headache, the cause of which is quite unknown, although many theories have been advanced, practically all of them unsupported by acceptable evidence. It is probably related to some functional irregularity of cranial circulation. The headache is painful, sometimes only on one side of the head, but often on both, and is generally preceded by depression, irritability and visual disturbance. It occurs in 5 to 10 per cent of the population, so that its cure or control is a definite medical challenge.

That challenge was accepted by the late Dr. William G.

Lennox of Harvard University, one of the leading authorities on epilepsy in the United States. Working with ergotamine, the alkaloid of ergot that had been isolated as late as 1920, Lennox and his associates devised a routine that had dramatic results. Injections of ergotamine relieved migraine in 90 per cent of all patients and all attacks, and the headache often stopped within fifteen minutes after the injection, although sometimes it took a little longer. Taking the drug by mouth was much slower in bringing relief and in severe cases often failed.

Lennox and his associates never claimed that ergotamine was a cure for migraine, but its ability to control attacks was so striking that it has remained the chief drug in bringing relief to these sufferers. The dose can be given as often as necessary and apparently does not lose its efficacy upon repeated use. But there is, as in all ergot derivatives, a danger of ergotism if too large a dose is used too frequently.

The Harvard scientists also found that in certain cases of migraine, ergonovine was preferable to ergotamine, because the former could be taken by mouth, which is unsatisfactory with ergotamine. But ergonovine is less effective, although it has less undesirable effects upon the stomach and intestines than may happen with prolonged use of ergotamine.

The results of this work on migraine touched off a lot of research on the effects of ergot alkaloids in patients having a disease caused by poisons entering the thyroid gland. Ergotamine has also been tried to relieve the itching often found in jaundice, cirrhosis of the liver, leukemia and Hodgkin's disease. But the results have been unsatisfactory, and what were called ergotamine "accidents" were too frequent to warrant further trials, especially as there were some cases of gangrene and a few deaths.

However, the Harvard scientists insist that with the proper dosage, administered with careful supervision, ergotamine "is a safe and useful drug and that no serious complications have been reported from its use in the migraine syndrome."

Such guarded and skillful use of ergot does not alter the fact that it is a highly poisonous drug. Improper or too long-continued dosage is courting the danger of an attack of ergotism that in advanced cases could lead to the loathsome condition of the peasants who had St. Anthony's Fire. Such a contingency rarely happens today, for all careful physicians are alert to watch for the first symptoms of ergotism.

None of the ergot alkaloids can be given to patients with liver disease, and in a few other conditions their use is hazardous. Of course those girls who take large doses to produce an abortion are simply courting acute poisoning with ergot, resulting, if the dose is too large, in vomiting, diarrhea, violent thirst, itching and tingling of the skin, often followed by confusion and unconsciousness, or even death.

Such cases of acute ergot poisoning are rare. But chronic ergot poisoning is much more common, due to too large doses and protracted administration. Some obstetrical cases require small doses of ergonovine for considerable periods after the birth. There are other conditions that need one of the alkaloids for an appreciable time. In all such cases there is the danger that a too long-continued therapeutic dose may initiate the first symptoms of ergotism. These nearly always start with a constriction of the blood vessels and interference with normal blood flow to the extremities. This may be followed by headache, nausea, vomiting, diarrhea and some dizziness and a feeling that insects are crawling over the body. Ultimately, of course, the much more serious gangrene may set in and heroic methods are needed to control its spread. Two of the most useful drugs to offset ergot poisoning are papaverine, one of the alkaloids of opium, and atropine, derived from belladonna.

With so many useful attributes and so many hazards in its

careless use, it is no wonder that there are conflicting views about ergot. Dr. H. W. Youngen, Jr., has called it "a veritable treasure house of pharmacological constituents." And Dr. G. M. Hocking headed his article with the caption "Ergot: A Blessing and a Scourge." It is obviously both, and the annual consumption of it is large. Before the last war, most of it was imported from Spain, Russia, Portugal and Germany—all of it the ergot of rye, for other ergots (wheat, grasses, etc.) are not permitted.

With the advent of World War II and the interruption of European imports, the United States began the growing of rye for ergot production in Minnesota, Wisconsin, North and South Dakota, Illinois, Indiana and Nebraska. The United States total needs are very large, in some years as much as a million pounds of raw ergot. Some American farmers shun ergot culture, because of the danger of infecting other crops. In Europe the collection of ergot is mostly a peasant industry, the diseased spurs being picked by hand. A few European growers have special milling machinery that separates the good grain from the ergot, and practically all American ergot is so harvested.

LSD

The most dramatic and least savory part of the story of ergot started in a laboratory in Switzerland in 1943. The cryptic initials LSD stand for a formidable chemical formula for lysergic acid diethylamide, a drug that hit the front pages of newspapers and magazines with somewhat deplorable results. LSD is a derivative of ergot, but its target, instead of being the uterus or migraine, was a direct attack upon the brain, perhaps not unlike mescaline, the hallucinogenic drug derived from an American cactus.* This was so much favored by the late Aldous Huxley that he wrote a book about it.

* An account of this cactus and mescaline will be found in the writer's *Narcotics: Nature's Dangerous Gifts.* Dell Publishing Co., New York, 1963.

Limited amounts of LSD were released to psychiatric institutions, because the production of a drug acting on the brain opened up promising avenues of research. The very concept that a laboratory-hatched derivative of ergot would directly affect the brain was intriguing to the scientists. They perfectly realized that such studies might be hazardous, even if the drug was administered in microscopic doses. It was, and the results were bizarre.

One patient, a twenty-nine-year-old woman in a state of deep depression and on the verge of suicide, recorded to the doctor that:

I had the sensation as in my first LSD treatment of a snake curling up around me. I felt very sick and dizzy. I then began to see serpents' faces all over the wall.*

Some uncharitable observers might suggest to the lady that quite similar symptoms could be conjured up in delirium tremens! Her obsession with snakes continued, however, when she reported that:

The Doctor came in and asked me how I felt and I told him that there were snakes everywhere. I had the sensation of being right in the middle of them. The Doctor asked me if it was like anything I had experienced before. I said it was a dream I had as a child. He asked me if I knew what that dream represented and I said, "Sex." He said "What sexual feelings could a small child of that age be having"—or words to that effect and I said I don't know. Actually at that minute I was right back as a small child with moving grass all around me and I could see snakes slithering through the grass. The whole atmosphere was as it had been when sexual incidents occurred with boys when I was about six or seven.*

If this seems a somewhat startling revelation of what LSD will do to the mind, it is not unusual, for the doctor who was tending this patient reported that:

* As quoted by R. S. de Ropp in *Drugs and the Mind*.

The snake, that great archetype which figures in so many myths from the plumed serpent of the Aztecs to the *nagas* of the Hindus, played a prominent role in many of the LSD experiences.

Sometimes as many as forty sessions of LSD treatment are necessary to help neurotic patients to bring about "this surging up of repressed experiences which have caused some of the most intense abreactions we have ever seen." If most of the patients have to wallow through many snakes or see innumerable spiders to conjure up "sexual incidents" of their childhood, there are some doctors who ask, "Is it worth it?"

The answer to such skeptics is that there are many mentally maladjusted people in the world, and that several leading psychiatric institutions turned to LSD with the hope that it was a new and effective tool. It is not a narcotic, does not induce sleep, and the patient is conscious of its working and effects, even when they are as unpleasant as those of the lady who saw too many snakes.

It was hoped that LSD would "unlock the dark mysteries of schizophrenia." Other possibilities were pointed out by Sir Julian Huxley, who wrote, "Nobody, so far as I know, has done any work on different types of psychologically normal people, people of high and low IQ, of different somatotypes, of different affective dispositions, or verbalizers and visualizers. This would be of extraordinary interest: we might find out not merely how to cure some defect, but how to promote creativity by enhancing the creative imagination."

An ergot derivative with such potentialities is obviously one that may have great possibilities in treating the mentally ill, but it has its dangers. Many psychiatrists and regular physicians are still a bit skeptical about the present and future value of LSD. Some of that uncertainty is due to the enormous amount of publicity regarding the drug. Already over a thousand papers on it have appeared in the technical press, not to speak of sensational and largely inaccurate lay articles. There is a well-founded suspicion that LSD has been an overplayed "wonder" drug, that it may, as so many have in the past, ultimately sink into obscurity.

Meanwhile active work is going on with what limited supplies are available. These are not as plentiful as they were initially, for rather sordid reasons. Not being a narcotic, it did not come under the restrictions of the United States Narcotic Act, and large amounts got into the hands of bootleggers, who were quick to see large profits in its sale to sensation-seeking individuals. Even such a responsible person as the late Aldous Huxley wrote of drugs that may influence the mind, "The development of drugs that change human behavior may well prove to be far more revolutionary than achievements in nuclear physics."

The bootlegged LSD certainly changed human behavior among a large group of individuals. One of them said it was "Instant Zen." Some drug addicts have abandoned the usual narcotics and now hold "LSD parties"—all this in spite of the hazards of self-medication with such a potentially dangerous drug. Cases are on record of psychotics who completely disintegrate after a single dose of the drug. The Swiss sponsors of LSD, co-operating with the United States government, are now trying to limit supplies of it to mental hospitals and other institutions, from where its final appraisal will ultimately come. But with all such hallucinogenic properties it will always be difficult to keep it out of the black market.

One irreverent observer has already said that tinkering with the mind is an immoral act. There is no question that this new drug does a lot of tinkering. Much of it may be of lasting value if it helps to rescue neurotic and psychotic individuals from the depths of the misery in which they live—not to speak of the anxiety of friends and relatives. If psychiatry, with LSD or any other drug, is able to cure such unfortunates, we can well forgive overoptimistic present statements and wait with hope that ultimately this derivative of the diseased kernels of rye, the cause of St. Anthony's Fire, will usher in a new era in medicine.

It has already done so among a group of experts who have tested its effects on hundreds of patients at the Napa State Hospital at Imola, California. One of the doctors in charge of these patients reported that they "become less anxious, less rigid, more spontaneous, more tolerant of ambiguity, more appreciative of esthetic and symbolic modes of expression, and less concerned over past and future." He also warns that these results are not always so favorable, for one patient reported that his joints were so smooth from grinding together that they felt "well-oiled" and this apparent "lubrication" lasted for weeks.

In that most perceptive book, *Drugs and the Mind* by Dr. Robert S. de Ropp, there is a chapter headed "The Chemistry of Madness" which describes the origin of LSD and its early effects upon the chemist who first synthesized it. Later in that book, Dr. de Ropp has this appraisal of it:

The treatment appears to be of particular value in obsessional neurotics in whom damaging memories are particularly strongly repressed. In such cases the memory is often so deeply repressed and detached from consciousness that it cannot be recognized when resurrected by LSD. Such a memory may be brought out in serial form, each treatment bringing further details into consciousness.

That such a result may take as many as forty treatments is stressed by the doctors who have studied it.

Some physicians still insist, in spite of these reports, that the wisest course is to suspend judgment on this spectacular derivative of ergot. A few of them, acutely concious of the rise and fall of other "wonder drugs," have not forgotten what Dr. Oliver Wendell Holmes wrote in the middle of the last century:

I firmly believe that, if the whole materia medica could be sent to the bottom of the sea, it would be all the better for mankind and all the worse for the fishes.

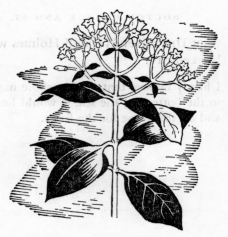

The Peruvian tree which controlled malaria

6. The Greatest Killer

IN THE SUMMER OF 1928 a curious and surprising conference met in Paris at the urgent request of the United States Department of Justice. Mr. William J. (Wild Bill) Donovan represented the United States, and to it went some rather disgruntled American manufacturers, traders and pharmaceutical magnates. Two Dutch gentlemen stayed quietly at Amsterdam and politely declined the invitation. They would be happy to meet their friends and associates, but hesitated to do so at the American embassy. They represented the tightest crop monopoly in the world, hence Uncle Sam's urgent invitation.

Monopoly is a forbidden word in the lexicon of United States antitrust authorities, and the Dutch gentlemen were naturally a bit shy at getting so close to jurisdiction as the United States embassy in Paris. It all started on April 23,

72]

1928, by the sudden seizure by the government of a drug in a warehouse in New York. The suit was somewhat elusively labeled "U.S. vs. 383,340 ounces of quinine." All of the drug had been imported from Holland and produced by a monopoly so well managed that not another country in the world could have provided that much quinine.

Under Dutch law monopolies were not only legal but encouraged, hence the bewilderment and caution of the two gentlemen from Amsterdam. They were urbane, sophisticated Europeans who could not understand or chose to ignore that they were "criminals" in the eyes of the United States Department of Justice. Having no real jurisdiction over them, the conference collapsed, and the world was forced to pay whatever price the Dutch chose to charge for quinine.

The fiasco of the Paris meeting did, however, lead the two Dutch "criminals" to come to Washington, where all indictments were quashed, the impounded quinine was released, and they signed an esoteric document called a "consent decree." No one has ever understood to what the Dutch consented, for they controlled the only real source of quinine, and all the world was clamoring for it, even if many thought the price too high.

To comfortably housed apartment dwellers or even to harried commuters in well-drained suburbs, this fantastic "trial" seemed a bit comic. But it was deadly serious to American health authorities, to the League of Nations, to its successor, the World Health Organization, the International Health Division of the Rockefeller Foundation and to the health officers of every tropical country. They well knew that in 1928 there was no other effective remedy for malaria, the greatest killer in the world.

Malaria

(A Lyric of India)

He lurks among the reeds, beside the marsh
Red oleanders twisted in his hair,
His eyes are haggard and his lips are harsh,
Upon his breast the bones show gaunt and bare.

The green and stagnant waters lick his feet,
And from their filmy, iridescent scum
Clouds of mosquitoes, gauzy in the heat,
Rise with his gifts: Death and Delirium.

His messengers: they wear the deadly taint
On spangled wings aloft and far away
Making thin music, strident and yet faint,
From golden eve to silver break of day.

It is next to impossible to exaggerate the curse that malaria has been for countless centuries. It has killed more people than all the wars, more than all the plagues, even the Black Death. And for the millions it does not kill it leaves a legacy of fever, chills, weakness and such a lack of ambition that the poor and destitute victims are usually left to swelter "in their own stench."

For over three thousand years no one knew either the cause of or the cure for malaria. For much of that time it was suspected that emanations from swamps or marshes were the cause of it; hence the coinage of malaria (mal-aire) by Torti, an Italian who thus perpetuated a grotesque error of which nothing remains today but his name for it, which was coined in the eighteenth century. Horace Walpole knew it as *malaria* in 1740; but before that, and in many places today, it is called ague or chills and fever, or even "the shakes."

So ravaging has been the disease that it depopulated whole regions, notably the Roman Campagna, upset military campaigns and made Africa all but uninhabitable to early European settlers. Sir Ronald Ross, who lived there for some years, called it the Dark Continent, because "For centuries the successive waves of civilization which have flooded and fertilized Europe and America, have broken themselves in vain upon its shores."

There are staggering charts that show virulent outbreaks of malaria in the fourth and fifth centuries B.C.; also in the sixth, seventh, eleventh, twelfth, eighteenth and nineteenth centuries of our era. Cicero knew it so well that he described Rome as "a pestilential city," and one section of the Imperial City was long called "The Vale of Hell." In seventeen of the southeastern states of the United States, there were, until recently, about 6 million cases annually in bad years and about 4 million in good ones. Most of these were not the malignant, deadly type of malaria; but in India for many years it killed over 1 million people annually. World mortality has been estimated at over 2 million per year, sometimes more.

Kings and queens have been plagued by malaria; so was Albrecht Dürer. Alexander the Great and Oliver Cromwell died of it, and some historians attribute the fall of Greece and Rome to its wholesale prevalence. The truth of this can safely be left to the historians, but all doctors in warm regions or in the steaming hot tropics know that no other disease has killed so many—hence the interest of our government in the Dutch quinine monopoly that produced its only known cure for many years.

As to the cause of malaria, there was only the foggiest notions for nearly eighteen hundred years. A Roman gentleman-farmer, a few years before the birth of Christ, came very close to the truth when he wrote "that in marshes there are animals too small to be seen, but which enter the mouth and nose and cause troublesome diseases." Not until November 6, 1880, was it known that malaria was caused, not by a mosquito, but by a microscopic organism found in the red blood corpuscles of man. This amazing discovery was made by a French physician, then only twenty-five years old. He was Charles L. A. Laveran, working as an army doctor in Algeria. He was certainly entitled to the Nobel prize if one existed then, for he pointed the way to the first inkling of what caused malaria.

The organism found by Laveran was named *Plasmodium,* and several different species were subsequently discovered, each causing a different sort of malaria. One causes periodic chills and fever, but seldom if ever kills. Another is the dreaded malignant type that, without treatment, kills in a few hours or days. While Laveran's discovery was epoch-making, it told us nothing of how the *Plasmodium* gets into our blood stream.

In 1902 the Nobel prize in medicine was given to Sir Ronald Ross, a British doctor then working in India, for telling the world how *Plasmodium* does get into our system with such devastating results. At Begumpet, Secunderabad, on August 25, 1897, Ross was the first to find this microscopic *Plasmodium* in the stomach of a mosquito. The implications were staggering and Ross knew it, for it explained the mystery of the transmittal of malaria from man to man. The mosquito does not cause it, but is the ever-present carrier of the organism that does. Ross attached no importance as to the kind of mosquito in which he found the parasite, but in a few months Giovanni Battista Grassi demonstrated that it is only the female of mosquitoes known as *Anopheles* that are the carriers of *Plasmodium.* Our ordinary pest mosquitoes in temperate regions are quite innocent of malaria infection, even if they are a bothersome nuisance.

Three mysteries of malaria, after eighteen hundred years of darkness, were thus solved just about the beginning of the present century. The Frenchman Laveran told us that the microscopic *Plasmodium* was the culprit, the Englishman Ross demonstrated the parasite in the stomach of the mosquito, and the Italian Grassi made it clear that only the female of the *Anopheles* mosquito could carry *Plasmodium*. All three of them are among the medical immortals, but Ross, more than either of the others, sensed what his discovery might mean in curing this age-old scourge.

On the evening of the discovery, Ross, who was a devout Christian, wrote a religious poem. And a few days later he wrote an account of the dosage of quinine necessary to cure the disease and for how long the patient must continue to take it. For years that dosage was followed by doctors throughout the world, in spite of the fact that no one knew the exact mechanism of the action of quinine on *Plasmodium*, if indeed it acts directly at all.

Only years later was it realized that the sex life of the parasite is so fantastic as to be almost unbelievable. When an infected mosquito bites a man, he injects into his victim a sexless, microscopic parasite while in the process of sucking blood. If the man is already carrying malaria parasites in his blood due to his having just recovered from a bout of malaria, these are of a kind known as *gametocytes, i.e.,* unmated male and female forms of *Plasmodium*, as yet quite virgin. But their virginity has been quickly lost in the stomach of the mosquito, and it is their young, sexless progeny that, when injected into our blood, are the real cause of malaria.

Upon such a set of facts man is a mere incident in the life history of the malaria parasite. It is only its sexless stage that can be lived in our blood stream, incidentally dooming us to a bout of malaria. But the ultimate perpetuation of *Plasmodium* depends only on the sexual mating of the parasites in the stomach of an *Anopheles* female mosquito. Such an apparently fortuitous set of circumstances ought to make malaria a rather rare disease instead of the greatest killer in the world. If we add the known allergy of *Anopheles* to sun and wind, and that they need at least four or five days to mature in quiet water, the wonder is that such fragile creatures survive long enough to bite anybody. But the mosquito population is enormous in warm regions, and in areas like India and much of Africa there is always an immense reservoir of malaria parasites in the blood of infected people. So the vicious circle has gone on for thousands of years, with no hope of a cure until about 1630, and no precise control of dosage until 1820.

The Peruvian Marvel

Everyone knows that quinine comes from the bark of a Peruvian tree, but few realize the astounding impact of the news that came from Lima in the early part of the seventeenth century. In that delightful capital city there lived a grandee viceroy and his wife. Fetes, parties, bull fighting and the social life of the Spanish aristocracy flourished brilliantly except for ever-present malaria.

One day about 1630, word was sent from Lima to Spain that on the eastern slopes of the Andes a tree had been found, the bark of which cured malaria. It sounded fantastic, for there was then no known cure. However, it touched off a drama that has lasted for nearly three hundred years. How could an infusion of bark, no matter how bitter, stop the misery of the ague? That it did so was quickly confirmed, and demands for the crude bark reached nearly astronomic proportions.

Many quite untrue legends are extant as to the discovery and first use of this marvel of Peru. It seems fairly clear that the Incas did not know the tree or its virtues, but a native name was attached to it, *quina*, later enlarged to *quina-quina*, literally meaning the bark of barks. That *quina* was also applied to the balsam of Peru, an entirely different tree, does not matter, for the malaria-curing tree has been called *quina* ever since, and from this native word came *quinine*.

The technical name of the tree was based on two errors made by the immortal Linnaeus, which were quite pardonable, considering the welter of legends that grew up soon after its discovery. What could be more improbable than a cure of the world's worst disease coming from far-off Lima? At any rate, Linnaeus swallowed a fantastically untrue legend by naming the tree *Cinchona*. This was to honor Countess Donna Francisca Henrique de Ribera, the wife of the Count of Chinchon, then acting for the king of Spain as viceroy of Peru.

Linnaeus thought, and for nearly three centuries everyone else "knew," that the Countess of Chinchon had been cured of malaria by quina bark, that she was so pleased with the remedy that she gave it to the poor, that it was hence called Countess' Powder and that finally she took it to Europe and was praised for introducing a cure for such a scourge. It is well known today that this pretty fiction is completely false, but Linnaeus did not know it then and hence *Cinchona* became the Latin name of quina, the great father of botany dropping an *h* in the process.

And so it has been *Cinchona* ever since, subsequent exploration disclosing that it comprises a group of shrubs and trees, nearly all on the eastern slopes of the Andes, stretching from Colombia through Ecuador and Peru into Bolivia—all in those days included in Peru. There are perhaps forty-five to fifty different kinds of *Cinchona*, but only a few are of any interest so far as malaria is concerned. Some are medium-sized trees, with lilac-like trusses of pinkish-white flowers, followed by seeds so small that it takes nearly 100,000 to make an ounce.

Traveling through a cinchona forest is a magical delight.

Mostly growing at between 3,000 and 9,000 feet elevation, the trees are never very common, because bark collection has been going on for practically three hundred years. Rainfall (80-125 inches per year) and constant mist or fog make these enchanting slopes a bit difficult to penetrate, so much so that one writer dubbed it a "Green Hell." Perhaps "Green Mansions" is a better term.

At Lima soon after 1630, the Jesuit fathers entered the picture so completely that ground cinchona bark was called Jesuits' powder. Under this name and under their highly intelligent and philanthropic guidance, it finally reached Europe in sufficient quantities to be of some use in the fight on malaria. Unknown to the good fathers, their sponsorship of the bark was to touch off riots in London within a few years.

They made many shipments of bark to Spain and of course to Rome, where malaria was so rife that many cardinals were killed by it while choosing three successive Popes. It was so fatal that these princes of the Church dreaded the death of a Pope and compulsory attendance at the Vatican to choose a new one.

Like some doctors today, there were European physicians in the seventeenth century who resisted a new remedy not sponsored by their profession. Especially were they skeptical of one that had only ecclesiastical backing, particularly by the Jesuits, whom many people distrusted. This apparent impasse to the introduction of cinchona bark in Europe was finally broken, at least in part, by a very remarkable Jesuit.

He was Cardinal John de Lugo, a scholar, a philosopher and an authority on ecclesiastical law. With the Thirty Years' War and the wreckage of the Reformation on his mind, the Pope had need of such a clear thinker as De Lugo. But that pillar of the Church had other things to consider. Traveling to Rome through the Campagna was little short of suicide, so rampant was the ague. And he knew of the deaths of many cardinals at the conclaves to choose a new Pope. If such eminent men could be struck down so quickly, what about the poor and helpless? At a big Jesuit congress in 1649, he had devoted much time to a discussion of the new remedy from Peru. It finally ended by Cardinal de Lugo spending the last ten years of his life in promoting the idea that Peruvian bark was a priceless gift of God because it cured malaria.

Against the opposition of the medicos, he distributed huge quantities of the bark in Rome and in other European cities. He studied the proper dosage of the crude infusions, for no one knew then that it was the undiscovered quinine in the bark that cured malaria. These potions must have been very unpleasant and extremely bitter, but thousands of Roman citizens gulped them down, for malaria was a curse that none could ignore.

Today it is easy to see that the "Powder of the Most Eminent Cardinal de Lugo" was indeed a boon to the Italian people, in spite of medical opposition. That opposition trickled all over Europe, with some notable exceptions, especially that of Dr. Herman van der Heyden, a Belgian physician, who published his *Discours et Advis sur les Flus de Ventre Doloureux* in 1643. It is the first European medical reference to cinchona bark.

Cardinal de Lugo died in 1660, a worn-out figure who was acutely conscious that his campaign to overcome medical opposition to Jesuits' Powder had partly failed. Perhaps he scarcely realized, at seventy-seven, that he was to become one of the immortals in the conquest of malaria. At his request he was buried near the tomb of Ignatius Loyola, and the inscription reads, again at his request, "John Cardinal de Lugo, a most eminent theologian of the Society of Jesus." For brevity and understatement it vies with the Paris inscription "Here lies Voltaire."

Thus, at the mid-seventeenth century, the use of cinchona

bark had two effective barriers against it: the overwhelming opposition of organized medicine and its sponsorship by the Jesuits. It is difficult today to gauge the violent opposition to the Jesuits all over Europe, particularly in England, just then in a bitter campaign against "popery," and especially the Society of Jesus. Any remedy favored by that Order was apparently doomed, and it certainly would have been but for the eruption of the most bizarre incident in the whole history of malaria. It was touched off by an Englishman, the most fabulous and successful quack in the world.

Robert Talbor

Little is known about the early life of this ingenious rascal, who, however, came of respectable parents. His father had been registrar to the Bishop of Ely, and Talbor spent a short time at St. John's College, Cambridge, afterward working as an apprentice to an apothecary there. It was here, no doubt, that he picked up enough medical jargon to float his ultimate claim to medical proficiency. England at that time was rife with malaria, it being very common in London and virulent in the county of Essex along the south coast. Talbor decided to go to this county and "cure" malaria. He never mentioned what was in the "cure," and it was unknown until his death. Soon after his arrival in Essex, reports began trickling back to London that real cures of the disease were actually happening by the administration of a secret remedy by a quack.

The staid Royal College of Physicians were at first skeptical, then indifferent and finally hostile. How could "a debauched apothecary's apprentice" cure malaria, when the greatest doctors in London were unable to do so? Of course, none of these learned practitioners dared to use the Jesuits' Powder, for England just then was violently anti-Jesuit. Charles II was a Protestant, but the Queen was a Catholic, and intrigue and dissension raged through Whitehall. No doctor who valued his reputation would think of using the Jesuitical cinchona bark. They preferred to bleed depleted patients, sometimes to death.

To all these fulminations Talbor paid not the slightest attention. But he went on with his secret remedy and cured so many patients that there came urgent calls from London to cure victims given up for lost by regular practitioners. Talbor made several clandestine trips to the capital, and his cures were uniformly successful. He absolutely refused to disclose what was in his remedy, but did announce:

Beware of all palliative cures, and especially of that known by the name of Jesuits' Powder, for I have seen most dangerous effects follow the taking of that medicine.

That seemed conclusive enough, so that whatever Talbor was using, it was not cinchona bark. He further tried to allay suspicion of quackery by writing:

I was resolved to do what study or industry could perform to find out a certain method for the cure of this unruly distemper (malaria). I consider there was no other way to satisfy my desire, but that good old way, observation and experiment.

Such unimpeachable sentiments should have quieted suspicion by London doctors, but there is little evidence that it did anything of the kind. Talbor kept on curing patients in Essex, but finally, at the request of many people in London, he moved to the capital.

The London of 1668 was eager to welcome the charlatan, and he soon became a fashionable quack, favored by the aristocracy and by everyone else who could afford his charges. Talbor, in order to clinch his pretensions of medical proficiency, issued a book in which he described himself as a feverologist. His term for it was *pyretiatro*. The book is a curious hodge-podge of "philosophy," "medicine" and rambling observations, but he carefully avoided any mention of the constituents of his cure. He was, however, soon to have his most august patient.

Charles II soon heard of the amazing reputation of Robert Talbor and of his acceptance by the London aristocracy, who blessed him as a miracle worker. Was he not curing malaria all over London, incidentally amassing a fortune? Quackery or no quackery, Talbor was almost a national hero. The King's physician scorned him, but Charles came down with malaria and demanded the services of Talbor. The consternation among the Royal College of Physicians did not move the King one iota. He insisted, and Talbor, refusing all demands of the King's physicians to divulge what was in his cure, promptly stopped the royal ague.

If the quack needed any bolstering of his reputation, this royal cure was the final touchstone of it. The King was so grateful that he called Talbor to Whitehall and promptly dubbed him Sir Robert Talbor. The royal favor went even further, for he demanded that the Royal College of Physicians make Sir Robert a member. The outraged doctors were warned that "you should not give him any molestation or disturbance in his practice." No affront to a learned body could be more devastating, but kingly prerogative in the late sixteen hundreds included somewhat autocratic powers, and the Royal College of Physicians was forced to submit.

Meanwhile, what was happening to cinchona bark, then universally called Jesuits' Powder, scorned by most English doctors, reviled by Talbor and incidentally the cause of riots in Whitehall? The outcry against popery and especially against the Jesuits was so virulent that placards were carried by the populace warning loyal Englishmen that the Jesuits "were going to poison the Protestant King Charles."

Under such circumstances, anything called Jesuits' Powder

was anathema, and it all but disappeared from British medicine. The King, however, had not forgotten Sir Robert, and sent him to his friend the King of France, whose heir was known to be suffering from malaria, as were many others in Paris.

Talbor's career in France reads like a fairy tale. Received with royal favor, housed in a palace, he promptly cured the King and his heir, earning the everlasting gratitude of Louis XIV, who sent him to Vienna and Madrid. He repeated his triumphs there and returned to Paris, where he was called the Chevalier and lived in courtly splendor.

Many famous Parisians begged him to give them what they called "The English Remedy" or "Talbor's Wonderful Secret for Curing Agues and Fevers." Among them were La Rochefoucauld and Mme. de Sévigné who went into raptures over *un homme divin,* declaring that he deserved a temple such as that of Aesculapius. The wits of Paris lauded him, and finding that a famous old French family was named Talbot, he became Sir Robert Talbot in France and Sir Robert Talbor in England.

Louis XIV became convinced that such a precious remedy should not leave France when Talbor returned to England. He offered to buy it if Talbor would divulge its ingredients. The quack politely refused, and the King promptly made an alternative offer. If Talbor would write the prescription of his remedy, the King would put it in a sealed envelope and lock it in a safe with the understanding that it would not be opened until Talbor's death. Being only about forty years old, with a long lucrative practice ahead of him, Talbor agreed.

The King paid him 3,000 crowns and a pension for life, and the now internationally famous quack returned in triumph to England. Distinctions were showered on him, among them was being made a fellow commoner of St. John's College, Cambridge. Soon after, in 1681, he died.

The dénouement would be little short of comic if it had not changed the whole European method of curing malaria. The King of France promptly released Talbor's formula, and its chief and only effective ingredient was the then hated Jesuits' Powder! The consternation in medical circles can only be likened to a revolution. Here was their despised quack, using for years the only real cure for malaria, keeping it a deadly secret, and finally telling the world not only that it was cinchona bark, but how to use it. Anti-Jesuit propaganda had already declined, and the final chapter was written by the inclusion of cinchona bark into the *British Pharmacopœia*.

Ultimate appraisal of Talbor's exploits cannot ignore the fact that he was a spectacularly successful quack, who kept secret for years the efficacy of cinchona bark in malaria. That the revelation of his secret put this Peruvian tree among respectable remedies and taught the medical profession how to use it, may mitigate his rascality. He never thought of himself as a quack; the monument he erected for himself in Trinity Church, Cambridge, inscribed by himself, before he died, reads thus:

> The most honorable Robert Talbor, Knight and Singular Physician, unique in curing Fevers of which he had delivered Charles II of England, Louis XIV, King of France, the Most Serene Dauphin, Princes, many a Duke, And a large number of lesser personages.

Two Young Frenchmen

By the end of the seventeenth century cinchona bark, no longer stigmatized as Jesuits' Powder, became the worldwide remedy for malaria, and huge shipments came from Peru and

Bolivia. So large was the trade that worried governments sent out explorers to look into not only the supplies but the actual identity of the different species of *Cinchona*. Some were useless and others seemed superlatively good.

For a hundred and twenty years this wholesale administration of the bark was the only effective remedy for malaria, but many thoughtful doctors began wondering what it was in this bark that had the property to kill the cause of malaria. Attempts to isolate this hidden active principle baffled scientists for years, and no one came up with a convincing answer until 1820.

Then on September 11, 1820, came electrifying news from a laboratory in Paris. Joseph Pelletier, then thirty-two years old, and Joseph Caventou, only twenty-five, announced the discovery of the alkaloid in cinchona bark that cured malaria. Because the native name for the bark was *quina*, they named their discovery *quinine*. So it has been ever since, called quineen' in every country in the world, but in the United States the vernacular is kwy'nine, or even kwin'in in Virginia!

However it is pronounced, its discovery was one of the greatest of scientific feats, because quinine is among the few real specifics found in the plant world. It revolutionized the treatment of malaria, as it was possible to give a measured dose of the pure alkaloid instead of the nauseous bitter brews that had been obligatory since 1630.

Other alkaloids have also been found in this extraordinary bark, most of them of only scientific interest. But one of them is life-saving. For people with that form of heart disease known to the profession as auricular fibrillation, this other alkaloid, called *quinidine,* steers the heart back to a normal rhythm.

But the great discovery, by Pelletier and Caventou, not only changed the whole treatment of malaria, it ultimately fired the French nation to accord these young scientists the unprecedented honor of a monument to them. In the Boulevard St. Michel there stood, until the Second World War, a bronze statue of these scientists in their academic robes, inscribed to the "discoverers of quinine." The idea of the monument originated in French scientific societies, and contributions came from all over the world. It was christened in 1900, but during the occupation of Paris in World War II, vandal Germans melted it down. A new and different monument was erected on the same site in 1951.

Unlike Robert Talbor, these French chemists refused to patent the drug, and made its manufacture available to anyone any where with the requisite skill. By 1823 a factory for the manufacture of quinine was opened in the United States at Philadelphia, resulting in an amusing and colorful episode in the Mississippi Valley.

The treatment of malaria at that time, at least in Philadelphia, still consisted in bleeding patients nearly to death. In Arrow Rock, Missouri, there lived a colorful general practitioner, by name John Sappington. He knew of the discovery of Pelletier and Caventou, and had little use for blood-letting. Consequently he sent his son to Philadelphia to buy a few ounces of the new remedy, but by an error his messenger came back with that many pounds! Quinine at that time cost about $10.00 an ounce, and Dr. Sappington was in financial difficulties.

With characteristic ingenuity, and some thought a dash of quackery, he concocted a remedy called "Dr. Sappington's Pills," mostly pure quinine, and induced the pastors of churches to have the bells rung in the evening to remind the people to take them. In the malaria-ridden Mississippi Valley there could hardly have been a better therapy, and the doctor waxed so rich that he left a fortune to a foundation for the education of poor farm boys.

Perhaps because he smarted under the implication of

quackery, he published in 1844 a little book on fevers in his region in which he confessed that the chief ingredient of his pills was quinine. It is one of the rarest of medical Americana and a landmark in our early treatment of malaria. He should thus be honored for introducing a remedy into a whole section of the country, only a few years after its discovery. His treatment was far superior to that in Philadelphia, and he materially helped in the conquest of a disease that threatened the westward expansion of his country. His ultimate inclusion in the *Dictionary of American Biography* certainly should remove him from the category of quackery, because he well knew the truth of what Sir William Osler was to write about malaria in 1917: "Treatment. This is comprised in one word: Quinine."

Crisis in Cinchona

With the isolation of quinine in 1820, the medical world was equipped for the first time with an effective, measurable remedy. Quite naturally the demand for bark with a high quinine content quickly became enormous. Millions were dying annually of the scourge, especially in India, Africa, Java, Greece and in many parts of Europe.

The scramble for bark became so great that private and governmental monopolies devoted to cornering the market were started in Peru and Bolivia. Bark collecting had always been a crude business carried on by Indians, and neither the bark monopolies nor the Indians knew anything of the value of the bark until it was possible to test its quinine content.

Such testing soon disclosed that the highest-yielding barks came from northern Bolivia and adjacent Peru, and such areas were cruised by Indians so extensively that year by year they were forced to go deeper into the forest for their supplies. No one had paid any attention to Antonio Ulloa, who wrote in 1735, "Though the trees are numerous they have an end." Also ignored was the Jesuit warning a hundred years before, that wholesale bark stripping, which, of course, killed the tree, must be followed by planting a new one. It seems never to have entered the minds of anyone to cultivate this priceless boon to mankind.

Two of the greatest colonial powers in the world became alarmed at the dwindling bark supplies from South America and saw little hope of curing the people, for whom they felt a definite responsibility. England, with malaria-ridden India, and Holland with millions of natives in the Netherlands East Indies, both determined to do something to assure future supplies of bark.

The Dutch moved first by sending J. C. Hasskarl, of the Buitenzorg Botanical Garden, to South America to collect seeds and plants of *Cinchona*. He sailed on December 4, 1852. It is useless to trace his perilous journeys through the forests of Peru and Bolivia, because his mission was a failure. He sent thousands of seeds to Java, but they were of relatively useless varieties.

His final effort was a demand for a Dutch warship, which sailed from Peru to Java in August, 1854. On it Hasskarl had collected five hundred young plants of a high-yielding variety and a large quantity of seed. Upon arrival at Batavia, all but seventy-five plants were dead; the survivors and the seeds were planted in a mountainous part of west Java and Hasskarl put in charge. Thousands of seedlings were produced and the young trees set out in plantations, where it naturally took some years for them to develop enough bark to be tested. Practically all of them were worthless so far as the extraction of quinine was concerned.

While in Bolivia, Hasskarl visited La Paz, then the cinchona capital of the world. There he met the Dutch consul who became so interested that he ultimately sent to Java thousands of seeds of many different species of cinchona, all of which were planted with the Hasskarl trees, and ultimately proved just as worthless. The score of these failures totaled nearly two million trees and no one knew how many thousands of guilders. The private tea planters of Java called this cinchona venture "The Government Folly."

England moved more slowly, more cautiously, and at a far greater expense. In December, 1859, a British expedition sailed for South America with Clements R. Markham in charge. Knowing little about botany or horticulture, he took along four younger men who were better-equipped. Their travels and discoveries are all recorded in Markham's *Peruvian Bark*, published in 1880. He there praised his expedition and said that his "introduction of Peruvian bark trees into British India and Ceylon is now an assured success." It would be difficult to crowd more error into so few words, for twenty years later more than a million Markham trees were cut down because their culture for the extraction of quinine was completely unrewarding.

This British fiasco merely illustrates why the Dutch venture also failed. Very few Peruvian or Bolivian Cinchona species contain enough quinine to make extraction of the drug a practical manufacturing proposition. All the British could do, with India clamoring for quinine, was to extract the *total* alkaloids of their poor bark and make it into an antimalarial, which is inferior to quinine. This drug was sold at a very low price or given away at the post offices throughout India. It was frankly a stopgap, because quinine extraction was next to impossible from nearly all the Markham trees.

Thus, by the opening of the United States Civil War, neither the British nor the Dutch had a sure source of quinine. Its extraction, if the quinine content of the bark is less than 3 per cent, is impractical, and one of the Dutch experts wrote that "it was considered that American barks with 3 per

cent quinine were of very good quality." But the vast majority of either Dutch or British trees yielded less than 3 per
cent. This, after years of work and the expenditure of millions of dollars, ranks as the worst horticultural fiasco ever
known.

Manuel Hatches the Monopoly

After those drab failures, one can scarcely blame the Dutch
or British for looking with a fishy eye on any *Cinchona* seed
offered for sale. But from just around the corner there burst
a brilliant refutation of such skepticism. While Markham
was in Peru, he appears never to have met another Englishman who had lived for years at Puno, on the shores of Lake
Titicaca and close to the border of Bolivia.

His name was Charles Ledger and he knew more about
Cinchona bark than anyone on the Markham expedition. For
years he had an invaluable Indian servant, Manuel, who
knew perhaps better than Ledger where rich *Cinchona* trees
were to be found. Ledger and Manuel had often been on
hazardous expeditions into the jungles of Bolivia and had
sold their high-yielding bark to British and American quinine manufacturers.

Ledger, in fact, was a bark trader, and one day suggested
that Manuel should go to a grove of particularly high-yielding trees that Ledger had seen some years before. Manuel
was to wait until a good crop of seeds could be harvested. The
site was in a remote corner of Bolivia, near the headwaters of
the Rio Beni. This is a rushing torrent, dangerous even for
balsa rafts, but it ultimately becomes quieter and flows into
one of the upper tributaries of the Amazon.

Manuel returned some years later with fourteen pounds of
seed and a flimsy tale of the tardiness of the trees to produce
a crop. His fate was to have violated a law of the Bolivian

government forbidding the collection of *Cinchona* seeds for export. He was later thrown into the jail at Coroico, well beaten, half starved, and finally died there—a tragic reward for an Indian who unwittingly sparked the quinine monopoly.

Ledger was in a quandary as to what to do with the seeds, as no one knew better than he that their ability to germinate would soon fade. He finally sent the whole batch to his brother George in London, with instructions to offer them to the British government for their Indian cinchona plantations. The government, rather sensitive to criticism of the Markham venture and skeptical of just any seed from South America, would not touch the Ledger seed.

George then went to Holland and offered the 14 pounds of seed to the government for their Java plantations. The thrifty Dutch, no doubt dubious about some unknown seed from Bolivia, agreed to take only one pound of the Ledger seed and paid George 100 francs, with the promise of a further payment of £24 if the seed turned out to be of any value. This seemed highly unlikely in view of their former failures.

George Ledger went back to England and literally hawked the remaining thirteen pounds of seed around the streets of London, but found no takers. He did, finally, run across a British Indian cinchona planter, home for a holiday, who bought the lot for an undisclosed price. He set sail for India, went completely sour on his purchase, and exchanged them at the British Indian cinchona plantation for seeds of another variety.

So, after all, the thirteen pounds of Manuel's seed went where Charles Ledger had suggested. No one knows today how the British Indian officials muffed the delicate operation of germinating these seeds. This much is known: they lost nearly all the seedlings, and the few that germinated never reached maturity.

The single remaining pound of Ledger seed was sent by the Dutch to Java in December, 1865. The Netherlands Indies cinchona experts looked with a somewhat fishy eye on this fresh shipment, for they were smarting under the ridicule of past failures. If they had but known it, that single pound of seed, upon the most conservative estimate, was worth anything from ten to twenty, and some later guesses said fifty million dollars, for upon it was built the world monopoly of quinine.

No one in Java expected any miracle from this pound of Ledger seed, but, like all other shipments, they were planted and cared for with the exacting techniques they demand. The seeds are almost microscopically minute, and very subject to the dreaded "damping-off," which may wipe out a whole seed bed overnight. The Dutch conquered these hazards, and within a year or two had 12,000 young Ledger seedlings.

Their subsequent handling of them is perhaps the finest example of tropical horticulture. Welding genetics, chemistry, soil science and ecology, their ultimate triumph reads almost like the more lurid and improbable science fiction. If the Dutch were hatching a monopoly in 1867, they never dreamed it, but today it is scarcely possible to exaggerate their obvious monopoly of horticultural science.

As the Ledger trees grew, but were still too immature to flower, the Netherlands Indies Cinchona Plantation sent to Holland for a young chemist to evaluate the bark. He was J. C. B. Moens, who arrived in Java in 1872. As he well knew, most of the two million *Cinchona* trees in Java never yielded much over 3 per cent of quinine, as a rule much less. Nearly all of these were mature enough to flower and set seed.

Moens carefully collected small strips of bark from the younger Ledger trees, took them to the laboratory and could scarcely credit his senses. Some of them tested over 8 per cent quinine, later samples 10 per cent and many 12-13 per cent.

A less phlegmatic people than the Dutch would have succumbed to some sort of delirium, for such figures meant final
domination of the world's quinine market.

Domination, however, was so far in the future that the
Dutch easily controlled their delirium, for no one knew better than they that the hazards were still formidable. The
flower structure of *Cinchona* is so arranged that self-pollina-
tion is impossible and cross-pollination, and hence hybridiza-
tion, not only likely but certain.

How, then, could they maintain the sexual purity of the
Ledger trees, once they were old enough to come into flower?
Three methods were evolved: one of them demanded the de-
flowering of all adjacent cinchona trees of the older lots. Perhaps only a geneticist can understand the magnitude of such
a task, but it was carried on for several seasons, until the
Ledger trees were ready for the second alternative.

This demanded the clearing of remote forest tracts, with
no cinchona in them, and so far away from the older plantations that neither bees nor the wind would infect them with
foreign pollen. Into this safe harbor the best of the Ledger
trees finally came to anchor, and the worried officials might
be assumed to have earned a rest.

Resting, except after a midday Javanese meal, was actually
far from the Dutch idea of future dominance of the quinine
market. Their only source of quinine at this point was the
two million trees of the older relatively worthless varieties.
But they knew that a few thousand Ledger trees, however
sexually pure in their mountain retreat, were a long way
from producing the millions of trees it would need to keep
the world supplied with quinine.

Carefully and methodically they began harvesting these
older trees, thus safeguarding the off chance of cross-pollination, and providing a supply of bark, even if it was far inferior to the Ledger trees. This went on for several years,

mostly at a loss, but aimed at the replacement of the stripped plantations with the new Ledger trees, which had meanwhile been christened *Cinchona ledgeriana.*

This tree developed a further hazard to future dominance. As a cultivated tree it does poorly on its own roots, which might well have doomed the whole venture, because such weaklings might never flower or set seed. Again Dutch horticultural skill sailed over this hurdle by grafting Ledger seedlings on the roots of a more vigorous variety. This became standard practice, so that millions of grafting stock were raised and so timed that they were ready at the proper moment for the insertion of the Ledger scions.

For years the private tea and coffee planters in Java had been jeering at the government's "futile" cinchona venture. No private planter would touch it. For one thing, a tree is planted, and ten to fifteen years later cut down, for the whole bark is the only harvest. But tea and coffee plants persist, with an annual harvest.

The picture changed almost overnight, when the Netherlands Indies Cinchona station announced its willingness to distribute seeds of these fabulous Ledger trees in 1877, just twelve years after their arrival in Java. Gradually the private planters took it up, now grateful enough to the authorities, not only for the seeds, but for guidance as to the exacting demands of a tree that can easily fail. For years the planters kept on increasing their plantings, and just before World War II, there were one hundred ten private cinchona plantations in Java.

The government cinchona station bowed out as a commercial source of quinine, but still sold or gave away seeds from the Ledger trees. Nearly all of the foreign governments that accepted these seeds failed to grow them. The American attempts in California were, of course, merely comic. The English in Jamaica, the French in Indo-China, the Belgians in the Congo and the British in India and the Federated Malay States—all failed, perhaps because they lacked the green thumb of the Dutch.

So successful were the Dutch plantations and so profitable were some of them, that American and British health officers began a campaign in the medical and lay press, ending up with the horrid suspicion that they were making too much money. The fact that these plantations were the source of the only cure for malaria, and that the Dutch absolutely controlled it, sparked the equally horrid suspicion of a monopoly.

How It Works

Of course, it was the tightest crop monopoly in the world and by far the best-managed. The planters in Java, like many other farmers, were apt to overproduce, and they did so several times on a disastrous scale. The European quinine manufacturers could then beat down the price of bark so that the planters were threatened with ruin. Finally they petitioned the government of the Netherlands Indies for the right to build their own quinine factory in Java. It ultimately became the largest quinine factory in the world.

In spite of this, the overproduction of bark, the greed of both the planters and the European manufacturers put the quinine business in a somewhat precarious position for one basic reason. No one can ask a planter to grow a crop that cannot be harvested until years hence, unless he is guaranteed a reasonable price for it at harvest time. No individual quinine factory dared to guarantee such a price, for ten to fifteen years hence it might be possible to buy the bark for much less.

This apparent impasse led both the planters and the manufacturers to go into several huddles. Instead of fighting, why not co-operate? Thus was born the Kina Bureau, located in Amsterdam, kina being the Dutch word for quinine. It began operations in 1913, and has been well cursed ever since, in spite of its remarkable record of efficiency. It was organized with five representatives chosen by the Java planters and five from the European quinine manufacturers, and these ten gentlemen picked an eleventh, who must have nothing to do with growing cinchona or making quinine. To these eleven men the planters and manufacturers delegated absolute power.

The Kina Bureau set quotas for planting, the price to be paid for bark, the amount of quinine to be manufactured and the ultimate world price. Of course no American could join such an unholy "combination in restraint of trade." But American manufacturers who bought bark, and traders who sold Dutch quinine to them were forced to go hat in hand to Amsterdam, where the Kina Bureau told them the facts of life. It was, of course, the Kina Bureau that the United States government attempted to curb at the Paris meeting of 1928. Having no real jurisdiction, however, it curbed nothing.

As to the price of quinine, the Dutch still claim that no drug of its importance is so cheap, which is generally true, especially when compared to the price of many American pharmaceuticals. They point out that one such American pill may easily retail at one-half dollar, compared with about three to four cents for a 5-grain quinine pill. Hence they become a little impatient at American criticism of the "prohibitive cost of quinine." It takes about 15 grains a day, for a few days, to abort an attack of malaria, and the total cost is far less than the price of a local movie.

What complicates the picture is that hundreds of millions do not have the price of that movie, any more than they can afford quinine. But, as the Dutch point out, that is an economic problem having no more to do with the production of quinine than the inability of impoverished people to buy a car. Only governments and philanthropic organizations can cope with such a problem.

The Dwindling Empire

Up to the beginning of World War II, the Dutch monopoly had flourished very vigorously—ever since they put Java into real quinine dominance. Fortunes were made in it. Just before that war started the United States government bought from the Kina Bureau 13 million ounces of quinine for the armed services. But three clouds on the horizon already pointed to the beginning of the end.

One was the elaboration of an old German formula in a Swiss laboratory that made commercial production of DDT a possibility. It reduced the mosquito population and hence malaria in the United States by something like 90 per cent, making it one of the quickest and most effective of all public health victories. Its use throughout the world, or its substitute analogues, may well conquer malaria in a few more years. This, of course, already has reduced the demand for quinine so drastically that the business looks far less rosy than it did a few years ago.

The second jolt was the synthesis of two purely artificial drugs that many doctors claim are superior to quinine. One was found at the Liverpool School of Tropical Medicine and is now manufactured by Imperial Chemical Industries under the name Paludrine. This is marketed throughout the malarial areas of the British Commonwealth, as well as in the Far East. An American variant of it, discovered at Johns Hopkins University, is sold under the name of Aralen. With the gradual reduction in malaria, both these drugs, as well as quinine, must find a dwindling market.

The third and most serious blow to the Dutch was, of

course, the loss of the Netherlands East Indies, for their horticultural skill had made that fertile island not only dominant
in quinine, but a huge source of tea, coffee, rubber, sugar,
kapok, sisal, palm oil and cocaine. How these crops, none of
which is native to Java, will fare under the republic of Indonesia remains to be seen.

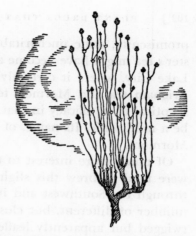

Chinese subshrub that yields ephedrine

7. From Shen Nung to Brigham Young

AFTER THIRTY YEARS of incredible effort, Brigham Young consolidated Utah and the Mormon Church, established the greatest trading center in the West, initiated the first irrigation scheme in the United States by watering an arid valley, established factories and banks, and finally died in 1877 with a reputation as an organizer second to few. He left behind him a thriving community, seventeen wives and forty-seven children.

Also a legacy of his was a beverage, much older than Mormonism, but in Utah called Brigham tea or Mormon tea. In the arid Southwest this had been variously called Mexican tea, teamster's tea and desert tea. The early pioneers learned its value from Mexican Indians, who used it only for one purpose—the reputed control or "cure" of syphilis.

Because that affliction is not entirely divorced from sexual

promiscuity, some uncharitable critics suspected that teamster's tea might have become a fairly popular remedy at Salt
Lake City, where it certainly picked up its designations of
Brigham tea and Mormon tea. Modern medicine is a bit
skeptical of its efficacy in that disease, although it appears to
be a mild tonic. Its name, of course, is no reflection on the
Mormons.

Of much more interest to the curious are the plants that
were used to brew this slightly disreputable beverage. All
through the Southwest and in adjacent Mexico there are a
number of different, but closely related, low shrubs, green-
twigged but apparently leafless. They are among the most
primitive of all the world's flowering plants, belong to the
joint-fir family (Gnetaceae), and somewhat resemble a horsetail (*Equisetum*). Their antiquity is prodigious.

One of them, as early as 1848, had been botanically christened as *Ephedra antisyphilitica*. It was found wild from
Texas to Colorado and in Mexico. Its specific name perpetuated the notion that at least this species was good for that
disease. Later studies of *Ephedra* revealed that there were at
least a dozen or more different species of the group, all confined to the arid Southwest and Mexico. Several were once
thought to be valuable in the treatment of pneumonia, an
illusion long since shattered.

The plants are perennial, low shrubs with a woody base
and a cluster of green, wiry, stiffish, bitter twigs that are
faintly grooved and apparently leafless. It is only these green
twigs that were used to brew Brigham tea. The twigs are
jointed and at each joint are a few small scales that would
be its expanded leaf blades if it had any. The flowers are almost microscopic, without any petals, and the sexes are always
separate, so that there are both male plants and female. Only
the latter produce the berry-like and often attractively
colored fruit.

Neither Brigham Young, the Mexican Indians, southwestern teamsters nor any American botanist or pharmacologist of that day suspected that they were nearly five thousand years behind the times in attributing medicinal virtue to *Ephedra*. They never knew, and not too many of us do today, that a Chinese emperor about 2700 B.C. had written a pharmacopoeia mentioning a Chinese species of *Ephedra*, not for syphilis, but for a variety of other diseases. He was the Emperor Shen Nung, and his history need not be repeated here for the little that is known about him will be found in the section on rhubarb in the chapter on "The Cathartic Racket."

The botanists had long known that there were several different species of *Ephedra* in China, the Himalayas, Russia, Persia and even along the shores of the Mediterranean. But these were chiefly of taxonomic interest to the experts because of the diversity and remote antiquity of the group. Little or no attention was paid to Shen Nung, which is not very surprising. The latest edition of his pharmacopœia was published in A.D. 1596, in Chinese, and it contains hundreds of drugs derived from plants. Obviously many of these were merely old wives' remedies. Dr. K. K. Chen, one of the greatest of modern Chinese doctors, wrote of many of these: "The vast number of these Chinese drugs not only includes most absurd substances from which they are derived, but also articles such as opium, rhubarb, chaulmoogra seeds, croton oil seeds, cinnamon, mercury and many others, which, or products of which, are official in modern pharmacopœias."

In other words, among these Chinese plants there were some that are of outstanding importance, and *Ephedra* is one. For fifty centuries they were using an infusion of the green twigs as a tea for improving the circulation by increasing blood pressure, promoting perspiration, reducing fever and as a sedative for these afflicted by persistent coughing. It was sold throughout China by the herbalists and in many drug-stores. Even in Russia the candied fruits of another species were used in the treatment of respiratory disorders—mostly hay fever.

Such a battery of attributes naturally touched off a lot of research on this Chinese plant that provided remedies for so many troubles. What sort of a plant was it? Where did it grow and how was it harvested, and when? It soon became obvious that the leading shrub was *Ephedra sinica,* universally called mahuang in China, a plant only fourteen to sixteen inches high, its slender, green, leafless twigs looking not unlike those that yielded Brigham tea. Its tiny flowers are yellow, and the mature fruit, which is less than one-half an inch in diameter, is red and fleshy.

The wiry stems have been harvested for centuries only late in the fall, usually just before the first frost, because the herb-alists and the public believed that such late gathering much improved the efficacy of the drug. Modern research has completely vindicated ancient practice, for summer-gathered twigs are never so valuable as those picked near frosty weather. The twigs, of course, must be dried for packing and shipment, and it was soon found that artificial heat and too much humidity reduced the value of the drug. It must be air-dried rather slowly.

Just as in the southwestern United States, the Chinese plants thrive best in dryish regions, hardly ever growing under a forest canopy. They have been found in such places practically all over China and quite plentifully, which is fortunate, because the demand for the plant has been great all through recorded history and maybe long before. The chief Chinese sources are in Shensi, Honan, Szechuan, Shantung and Kian. In some parts of China another species of mahuang, known as *Ephedra equisetina,* is also collected, but it is less important than *Ephedra sinica.*

No one will ever know who first guessed mahuang might cure various ills that plague primitive people. Least of all, how could the Chinese know why it persisted through the centuries and through many dynasties, where culture, wealth and the arts flourished on a magnificent scale? Marco Polo does not mention it, but the last edition of the pharmacopœia of Shen Nung includes it as a precious drug, three hundred years after the Venetian left China.

Every herbalist and drugstore carried it, and all the many Chinese medical books described the plant and sang the praises of the drug, without in the least knowing why. And no one knew, for the better part of five thousand years, what the active ingredient of mahuang might be. China's contacts with the West were rather tenuous for many centuries, and it is doubtful if they ever heard that the tannin of Brigham tea had been isolated in America in 1876. Or that this tannin contained none of the active ingredients of the Chinese plant.

Such ignorance was finally cleared up neither in China nor in America. A trio of Japanese scientists were responsible for the isolation of an alkaloid that has since become world-famous. In 1885 Dr. G. Yamanashi, at the Osaka Experimental Station, isolated a rather impure sample of the alkaloid found in mahuang and died soon after, without naming it. Two years later Dr. Nagai and Dr. Hari, working on the same problem, isolated for the first time the pure alkaloid and, appropriately enough, called it *ephedrine*. Only a year after, in 1888, a huge German firm at Darmstadt also announced their independent isolation of ephedrine.

These basic and highly important discoveries were practically ignored by physicians in the United States for nearly forty years. They might still be, were it not for two highly trained scientists who startled Western medicine in 1924 by their carefully appraised report on ephedrine. There had been a few leaks of its wide use in China, and one of the explorers of the United States Department of Agriculture, in 1913, wrote to Washington that the Chinese *Ephedra* he had collected grew "on elevated wind-swept plains, and was much used by the Chinese as a medicine in urinary troubles." That is a long way from being of medical significance.

The introduction of ephedrine into America was the result of one of those happy accidents that are grasped only by those with the wit to see them. Two relatively young pharmacologists were in a drugstore in Peking in 1923, and one of them spoke fluent Chinese. They were told by the druggist about the wide use of mahuang, doubtless repeating much of the ancient lore but not too much else of use to enquiring young scientists. They determined to work on the plant and its alkaloid ephedrine, which was all but unknown, except as a proprietary remedy for asthma. This had been put out by a firm who heard the faint trickle of news about ephedrine which reached the United States between 1917 and 1921.

Both the pharmacologists have since run up spectacular records of achievement. One of them was Dr. K. K. Chen, born in Shanghai in 1898, who went to the University of Wisconsin in 1918, then took his M.D. from Johns Hopkins in 1927, and in between times served as Senior Assistant at Peking Union Medical College. Later, long after the ephedrine study, he became the head of the Research Department of one of America's leading pharmaceutical firms. Honorary degrees and all sorts of citations of excellence have been showered on Dr. Chen ever since.

His associate in their epoch-making study was Dr. Carl F. Schmidt, born in Pennsylvania, and an M.D. from the University of Pennsylvania. In 1922-1924 he became an Associate in Pharmacology at the Peking Union Medical College. Since then he has held positions of distinction in the world of medicine. This combination of two highly trained pharmacologists, one of whom was born in China, made a team that was unique. Who better than Dr. Chen could sift all the Chinese literature on mahuang and ephedrine, avoid all the old wives' tales, and appraise the valuable work done on the drug by earlier Chinese scientists? After clearing up some of these pharmacological uncertainties, the two young men started to work.

It would be idle to speculate as to whether they knew that their investigation would result in a medical upheaval in the United States and in Europe. They began with the basic study of the leading source of ephedrine, which was *Ephedra sinica,* the twigs of which contain only about 1 per cent of the alkaloid. The next in importance was *Ephedra equisetina,* which is a much taller shrub, growing from three to five feet high. A third source was *Ephedra distachya,* a shrub about the height of *Ephedra sinica.* All of them have a superficial resemblance to the horsetails, hence the Greek name of *Ephedra,* which Pliny attached to what we now know as *Equisetum,* of which a widespread species is *Equisetum arvense,* the common horsetail.

The next step was to appraise the studies of the Chinese pharmacologists who worked on mahuang before Chen and Schmidt. These earlier workers, between the isolation of ephedrine in 1887, and 1924, had emphasized the value of the drug in ophthalmology, for it enlarged the pupil of the eye and had been used for that purpose. But this soon waned, and so far as the West was concerned, ephedrine was all but an unknown alkaloid. Today it is one of the best known, widely used by physicians and the lay public.

The public has become so conscious of high blood pressure that, if they knew of it, they would have scoffed at the announcement that ephedrine unquestionably *increases* blood pressure. With most people over forty acutely afraid of high blood pressure and by diet and nostrums trying to avoid it, of what possible value was a drug that actually increases it?

As usual the public was wrong, for at least two important reasons.

There are people, and quite a few of them, who habitually suffer from too low blood pressure. Sometimes such people, from a change of posture, may have such a sudden fall in pressure that it affects the brain, and fainting or dizziness or disorientation inevitably follows. This is especially true in those who rise to an erect posture from a horizontal one, or have taken too much exercise. Ephedrine increases the blood pressure of such patients, besides having a useful effect upon the brain and central nervous system. If it is not life-saving, it makes the patient much less apprehensive, so that he feels better. It is not a permanent cure for habitual low blood pressure, but it is a valuable drug in such a contingency, although there are a few cases in which the symptoms do not return.

Its other, and much wider, use is in correcting the usual fall in blood pressure of those who have to undergo spinal anesthesia for operations. This can become alarming, and without correction even fatal. It is now almost routine to inject, with the procaine, a certain amount of ephedrine. And in prolonged operations, where the fall in blood pressure might become dangerous, another injection of ephedrine may be obligatory.

More complicated is the use of ephedrine in an alarming condition which physicians call complete heart block. This results in seizures of vertigo, dizziness and fainting (Stokes-Adams disease). Careful doses of ephedrine have been found useful in this trouble, but as such patients may have serious organic heart disease, the drug must be used with caution.

Far more common are the trying symptoms of asthma, hay fever and the common cold. Ephedrine cures none of these complaints, but it affords such temporary relief that its use by physicians and especially by the lay public is so great that the drug has become a major item among pharmaceutical manufacturers.

Bronchial asthma, as distinguished from asthma caused by other diseases, is a painful and irritating trouble, thought to be caused in many cases by a spontaneous or inherited allergy, *i.e.*, pollen, dust, molds, animal scuff, lint, feathers and possibly insecticides. It is not only distressing but it can be fatal, the nasal passages and bronchial passages to the lungs being partially or almost completely stopped up.

A favorite remedy (not a cure) was and still is, for many physicians, an injection of epinephrine. This substance is a human hormone, synthesized and put out under the trademarked name of Adrenalin, and still known to many only by that patented name. Epinephrine has a beneficial effect upon the spasms of asthma, and is widely used in these emergencies. Its chief drawback is that such injections must always be done by a physician, as it cannot be taken by mouth.

It soon transpired that the chemical structure of ephedrine and epinephrine (Adrenalin) were fairly close, and this led to the use of ephedrine in bronchial asthma. In the first place the patient can swallow the dose and its quite similar effects last much longer than those of epinephrine (Adrenalin). Today ephedrine occupies a commanding place in the treatment of asthma, just as Shen Nung said that mahuang was good for bronchial troubles five thousand years ago.

Its action in helping asthmatics is due largely to its ability to clear nasal passages and the bronchial ones leading to the lungs. No one suffers more from the failure of these organs to function properly than people with hay fever. This is a complaint due entirely to susceptibility to the spring pollens of the catkin-bearing trees (oak, pecan, willow, walnut, poplar, etc.), the summer pollens of grasses and the most virulent of all, the ubiquitous ragweed of late summer and early fall. This allergy, however, is a seasonal one, not to be compared with the far more serious bronchial asthma. Watery discharge from the eyes and nose, sneezing and irritation of the nasal passages—these are misery enough to demand a remedy.

The most commonly used corrective for hay fever, usually giving prompt relief, and in a few cases permanent cure, is ephedrine or one of its synthetic analogues. Where it is taken internally and also used as a spray or in ointments, the relief may come within a minute or two. There are innumerable proprietary remedies for hay fever, many of them containing ephedrine, and self-medication is all but universal. Those who take skin tests for sensitivity to particular pollens are advised not to use ephedrine for twelve hours before such tests, because it may prevent the appearance of positive reaction. The consumption of ephedrine by hay fever patients is tremendous, thanks to Drs. Chen and Schmidt, not to speak of the ancient Chinese emperor.

A few people suffer from an almost uncontrollable desire to sleep at any time of the day, but often sleep poorly at night and have more or less terrifying dreams. With the desire to sleep at inopportune times there is often a temporary weakness of the extremities. The cause of the disease is entirely unknown, but ephedrine is the drug of choice to control it. Fortunately the disease is rather rare, and the only rival to ephedrine in its control is the closely related amphetamine (benzedrine). Neither drug is a cure, but ephedrine is preferred by many physicians for the control of the trouble.

Because ephedrine is a stimulant to the central nervous system, as well as increasing the blood pressure, it is usually stopped about 5:00 P.M. to permit the too sleepy patient to have normal sleep at the usual time. If he cannot sleep normally on this regime, many patients are given a tranquilizing drug with the ephedrine. The stimulant effect of ephedrine and the need to control it are two of the few contraindications to its use, not only in these sleepy patients but with many others, especially if ephedrine is given more or less continuously as in hay fever or asthma. It has almost no other unfavorable reactions, except for patients with organic heart disease and a few other complaints, for which the watchful physician is always on the alert.

This stimulant action of ephedrine is often utilized in the treatment of patients in an alcoholic coma, poisoned by morphine or heroin, and for the suicidal attempts with massive doses of the barbiturates. It stimulates the central nervous system, increases respiration and usually lessens the degree of depression.

One final use of the drug is successful, usually when combined with prostigmine, in the treatment of "that tired feeling" that happens to some women, but few men, toward evening. That disease is discussed in the Chapter entitled, "The Helpful Poisoners," under the section dealing with the Calabar bean. Known as myasthenia gravis, it can be controlled by a mixture of ephedrine and prostigmine, and some patients "have been restored from complete invalidism to a normal existence by the use of ephedrine alone, but the results are rarely as dramatic as those obtained with prostigmine."—(Goodman & Gilman, *The Pharmacological Basis of Therapeutics*).

The cure or control of any of these diseases by the administration of ephedrine was completely unknown in the United States before 1924. While all this spectacular success cannot be credited directly to Drs. Chen and Schmidt, it was their work in the laboratory of the Peking Union Medical College which opened up vistas of lasting importance. Few scientists can claim greater credit. The initial sifting of the evidence, accumulated over a period of fifty centuries, brought a Chinese shrub and its alkaloid into modern therapeutics, and transposed Shen Nung's ancient lore into ephedrine—a drug now in every hospital and drugstore in the world.

A grateful public, as a final tribute to Drs. Chen and Schmidt, can never forget that in nine major diseases or complaints, and in some minor ones, they opened the door to their control or cure. The major diseases or complaints in which ephedrine has been helpful are worth repeating. They are:

Dilating eye pupils   Asthma
Increasing blood pressure Hay fever
In spinal anesthesia Compulsive sleeping
Heart block   Drug poisoning
Myasthenia gravis

Ephedrine did not at first have wide acceptance in the United States, and the American Medical Association did not admit it as a standard drug until three years after the initial paper by Chen and Schmidt. That same year of 1927 saw the synthesis of ephedrine in the laboratory, making the future collection of *Ephedra* twigs seem unnecessary. But as time went on, such was the growing popularity of the drug, there was active search for other species of *Ephedra* which would maintain ample supplies of ephedrine. At that time the sole source was *Ephedra sinica* from China. The demand was so great that the United States imported in 1940 nearly a million and a half pounds of the twigs. By 1952 the importation had shrunk to about forty-six thousand pounds, none of which came from China, as that government preferred to divorce itself from trade with the United States by the adoption of the Communist regime on September 21, 1949.

In the search for non-Chinese species of *Ephedra,* all the American species from the Southwest were found to contain no ephedrine, and if they had any medicinal value, it was not due to that alkaloid. The drastic reduction of imports and the failure of the American species to contain any ephedrine made the hunt for another species of *Ephedra* more urgent than ever.

Such a plant appeared to be *Ephedra gerardiana* from India. In the days of Chinese imports a considerable amount of *Ephedra sinica* came through Tibet for shipment from Indian ports. On the way the Chinese twigs were often found to be adulterated with this Himalayan relative of the original mahuang. Investigation soon disclosed that the Indian *Ephedra gerardiana* contained almost as much ephedrine as the Chinese plant.

Indian officials were quick to see the importance of this. Even if the Himalayan plant only contained 0.80 per cent of ephedrine, it was worth exporting. Better yet, why not extract ephedrine from it in India and export the pure alkaloid? This was done, most of the plants coming from that section of the Himalayas included in Baluchistan, which, after partition, belonged to Pakistan. Hence Indian trade in *Ephedra* and ephedrine soon waned after partition in 1947.

But *Ephedra gerardiana* was also native west of India. It is a twiggy shrub, easily harvested, and is found along the Himalayas from India, through Pakistan, Baluchistan, Afghanistan and Persia. It grows, depending on elevation, from eighteen inches to six feet high, and is so abundant in Baluchistan that "the abundant cheap raw material" appeared to warrant the opening of an extraction plant in Pakistan, in spite of the threat of synthetic ephedrine. The Pakistani officials, as late as 1957, were boasting that they had "a virtual world monopoly for the naturally produced drug."

Without much regard for such an optimistic prophecy, several other countries, including the United States, wondered if the world supply of the natural drug should be confined to these Pakistani enthusiasts. Cultivation of true *Ephedra sinica* appeared to be the answer, and this was done in Yugoslavia, Spain, Kenya, Australia and in the southwestern

United States. Some of these attempts were made with other species of *Ephedra* that contained profitable amounts of ephedrine, although the American culture in Oklahoma and other parts of the Southwest confined itself to the original Chinese species.

Today there is little danger of a shortage of ephedrine. The synthetic product, plus the cultivation of the plant, ensures a safe supply of the drug Shen Nung tasted five thousand years ago and said "was good for respiratory infections."

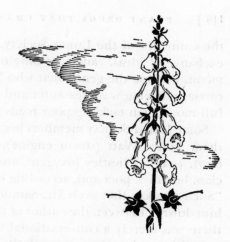

Foxglove, the only source of digitalis

8. "Wilt Thou Cure Thine Heart?"

It WOULD HAVE NEEDED a stout heart to stand the smoke of Birmingham, England, just before our Revolution. Then and ever since it has kept its lead as the greatest manufacturing city of the Midlands, and is second only to London in population. Buttons, screws, pins and needles, coal, iron, steel, tools, paper and glass—all poured their grime over a people who worked twelve hours a day for a pittance. One contemporary explained its phenomenal prosperity by saying "Its manufacturers and working people were brought up to be industrious and that from the early age of five or six years both sexes entered workshops where they were taught to act rather than to think."

That such a city should sprout a distinguished group of intellectuals seems almost as incredible as its mounting wealth. But, when it started in 1765, there was no doubt of the eminence of the Lunar Society. It was founded for "the exchange of ideas," and met only on the evening of the full moon, because the gentlemen who belonged to it found that carriage driving was pleasanter and safer with the help of the full moon than tackling poor roads in the dark.

Some Lunar Society members became world-famous, among them James Watt (steam engine), Josiah Wedgwood (pottery), Joseph Priestley (oxygen), and Erasmus Darwin, physician, botanist, poet and, according to a book by his daughter, "Such a talker that even Dr. Samuel Johnson could not talk him down." Between the author of the *Dictionary* and Darwin there was merely a conversational truce.

Such was the distinction of the society that foreign and native savants were honored to be invited. Among them was Sir William Herschel, the astronomer; Sir Joseph Banks, the instigator of Kew Gardens; D. C. Solander, the librarian of the British Museum; Adam Afzelius, a noted Swedish botanist; Benjamin Franklin, who went to talk electricity with Priestley, and Antoine Lavoisier, the aristocratic and brilliant French chemist, who was soon after guillotined by the Paris Revolutionary Tribunal.

One of the founders and perhaps the leading spirit of the Lunar Society was Erasmus Darwin, grandfather of the immortal Charles. He was an enormously fat, vain man, gross, dirty, untidy, and very irascible, but famous even then for his long, philosophical poem, "The Botanic Garden." Earlier in his career as a doctor, he had been friendly with a leading physician in the city, who was also a member of the Lunar Society. This was a Dr. William Small, who died in February, 1775.

At this juncture Darwin succumbed to one of the few really fine instincts of his life. His son Robert, also a doctor, was obviously too young to step into the shoes of Dr. Small. And on February 25, 1775, Darwin wrote to a quite unknown young doctor, offering his influence to secure for him the post made vacant by Dr. Small's death. In a letter a few days later, urging acceptance of his offer, he subscribed himself "your affectionate friend and servant—E. D."

Darwin was then just ten years older than his unknown correspondent, who, after profuse thanks, came to Birmingham and was accepted for the place. He was soon elected to the Lunar Society, and made a discovery since known to every doctor in the world. He also published a two-volume book that became a classic in British botany. Such was its success that it ran into its fourteenth edition by 1847. That Darwin's young protégé should achieve such meteoric flights corroded whatever instincts of generosity the older man had once possessed, and the sequel created a scandal. The young man's name was William Withering, then only thirty-four years old.

"The Disagreeable Ideas I have formed of the Study of Botany"

So wrote William Withering to his parents. He was then at the Medical School of the University of Edinburgh. His home was at Wellington in Salop (Shropshire), then and now among the pleasantest parts of rural England. His father was Edmund Withering, an apothecary at Wellington, and such was the snobbery of eighteenth-century England that no apothecary could be a "gentleman." That stigma was partially removed by his marriage to Sarah Hector, William's mother. She was the sister of Dr. Brooke Hector, a noted physician of Lichfield and quite wealthy. Edmund was also well heeled, so that William never had to pinch pennies.

His career at Edinburgh clearly pointed the way to future brilliance. Learning to play the flute, conquering the complexities of the bagpipes, playing rather poor golf, and participating in many social diversions—none of these stifled an extraordinarily active mind. Not yet twenty-five years old, he organized a "Society for Increasing the Knowledge of Latin," a language in which he read medical papers. One, prophetically enough, was on dropsy, for which no one then knew the cause or the cure.

The University of Edinburgh bristled with distinguished teachers. One of them was Professor Richard Pulteney, whose lectures on botany aroused the ire of William, but apparently left some residue, for a few years later he was preparing a major botanical treatise.

Finally, on July 31, 1766, William was awarded his diploma in medicine and had one foot on the ladder to fame. Like other reasonably affluent young doctors, there was the lure of the continent. But a brief trip to Paris with a French-speaking friend was cut short by the death of his companion after only a few weeks of sightseeing. William became disenchanted with the French, particularly with a group of young intellectuals. A smokeless capital with superb buildings, after the grime of the Midlands, charmed the young man, but he wrote to Wellington that the young men of Paris "displayed a moral laxity and a latitude of Christian faith." Especially revolting to Withering was a large party of society people sitting around an arena where animals were baited and "the spectacle turned into a torchlight butchery." It seemed to Withering far more brutal than the worst excesses of eighteenth-century British pugilism.

He was back in Wellington to spend Christmas with his family and soon began casting about for a place to hang his shingle. Wellington was well supplied with established doctors, so that an opening in nearby Stafford was eagerly grasped. It came by the death of a local doctor, and Withering settled there, as "local competition seemed moderate." It was only twenty miles from his home, and it was at Stafford that he quietly started on a career that ultimately made him world-famous.

But fame then seemed a long way off. Patients were few, and in his eight years at Stafford he never earned over £100 per year. This did not matter too much, especially after the death of his father, who left William all of his freehold property. Even before this legacy, he was "enjoying the best Society that that part of the country afforded." We hear of his taking part in concerts, joining an amateur dramatic society, using the bowling green and sometimes driving to Stratford-on-Avon. Here he joined the young bloods from London, Gibbon and Boswell among them, to see the immortal David Garrick in Shakespeare.

What we do not hear, perhaps because of eighteenth-century British reticence, is any hint of his love affairs, if he had any. One of his first patients at Stafford was the daughter of a prominent lawyer. She was Helena Cooke, just seventeen in 1767, and Withering wrote home about her with admirably restrained ardor. He insisted that she was proficient in "the harpsichord, the voice, the pencil, and every exterior accomplishment were already at her command."

This inflammatory effusion perhaps reflected his attitude toward matrimony, for years later he wrote two bits of advice. To a young bride:

It is quite out of character for a wife in your circumstances to *get* money; her proper mode of earning is to *save*. (Italics his.)

To another young bride:

I hope that my young friend will learn that vanity and ambition are not productive of happiness.

These sound but somewhat chilling statements no doubt explain why the romance ripened rather slowly, for not until September 12, 1772, were Helena and William united in a marriage that lasted until the end of their lives.

But in the five years it took for the patient to become his

wife, the beloved Helena sent him on many excursions to collect wild flowers, for she was an avid flower painter. Some have even given her chief credit in changing William's aversion to botany. Perhaps she should share this with the residue of Professor Pulteney's lectures. Whatever the cause, Withering became the most famous protagonist of botany of his period.

The time was ripe for it, and he had the wit and knowledge to realize it. Only a few years earlier, Linnaeus had astounded the learned world with his *Species Plantarum,* issued in 1753. For the first time this Swedish father of botany standardized the naming of plants and their arrangement in coherent sequence. But the book was in Latin, a language as unknown to the British public then as it is to most of us today.

With the *Species Plantarum* as a guide, and translating many technicalities into the vernacular, Withering began the slow accumulation of the data that resulted in *A Botanical arrangement of all the vegetables (flowers) growing in Great Britain, with an Easy Introduction to the Study of Botany.* There was no other such comprehensive book in English at the time; hence its tremendous popularity, leading ultimately into many enlargements and revisions.

The two volumes of the first edition were finally published in 1776, just a year after Erasmus Darwin invited Withering to begin the practice of medicine in Birmingham. All of his professional colleagues, including Darwin, knew that Withering had been working for years on the *Botanical Arrangement,* while also carrying on an increasingly arduous practice.

Such was the success of the first edition that Withering enlarged and revised it for a second edition, issued in 1787. Between 1776 and 1787 there was no other book in English that used the Linnaean system, and Withering's reputation among the flower-loving English was so great that the more sinister attributes of Erasmus Darwin came violently to the surface. He simply could not stand the eminence that had come to his young protégé.

He began the instigation of a scheme to translate Linnaeus' *Species Plantarum* into English. Withering, as the obvious expert, was offered the job, but could not do it, for he was deep in the preparation of his second edition. He offered, however, to help in some technicalities, especially modes of accentuation, and many of his suggestions were adopted by Darwin's associates in the scheme.

When the Darwin-inspired book appeared, there was no acknowledgment of Withering's help, and it stated bluntly that Withering's *Botanical Arrangement* was a mere translation of the work of another writer. This was so obviously absurd that the public was outraged, and there followed an exchange of correspondence and reviews that remind one of journalistic invective in our more primitive newspapers.

Perhaps some of Erasmus Darwin's envy was generated by the publication only two years before of another book by William Withering that was to make this Birmingham physician known throughout the world. It had nothing to do with the *Botanical Arrangement*, but that his young protégé should outstrip him in both botany and medicine was more than Darwin could tolerate.

The Foxglove

Dr. Withering spent a good deal of his time treating indigent patients who could pay nothing—sometimes as many as 2,500 per year. Also he regularly assisted at the Birmingham hospital and made frequent trips to Stafford and Shrewsbury. These were time-consuming and often involved an all-night carriage drive over indifferent roads. On one of these trips he stopped to change horses, and a local inhabitant asked if he would see "a poor old woman with dropsy." She was far gone, and the doctor had a poor opinion of her survival. But some weeks later, upon asking about her, he was amazed to hear that "she had made a good recovery."

It is perhaps the mark of medical genius never to ignore improbable "cures," even for dropsy, for which no doctor then knew the cause or the remedy. But it was often fatal, and Withering decided that on his next trip he would find out how such a quick recovery was possible. He ultimately explained it himself:

In the year 1775 my opinion was asked concerning a family receipt for the cure of the dropsy. I was told that it had long been kept a secret by an old woman in Shropshire, who had sometimes made cures after the more regular practitioners had failed. I was informed, also, that the effects produced were violent vomiting and purging: for the diuretic effects seem to have been overlooked. This medicine was composed of twenty or more different herbs: but it was not very difficult for one conversant in these subjects to perceive that the active herb could be no other than the Foxglove.

How he perceived it in 1775 will always be a mystery—perhaps another sign of genius. The foxglove had been included in the first edition of his *Botanical Arrangement,* but no medical virtue was attached to this showy biennial flower that is wild in England and over much of the continent. It was, of course, no stranger to Withering, for its handsome, tall flowering stalk with its hanging corollas was familiar to every gardener in England. It is first cousin to the snapdragon and second cousin to the beautiful *Paulownia* from China and Japan.

The foxglove already had an ancient history. One pre-Linnaean botanist had described it as early as the sixteenth century. This was Leonard Fuchs, a Bavarian physician and botanist, for whom our fuchsia was named. Scores of medical and botanical references to foxglove are scattered throughout the literature of the next two centuries, many of them ascribing to the plant dozens of medical virtues, all of which were either false or grossly exaggerated. At that time this was nothing to get excited about, for there were literally hundreds of so-called medicinal herbs prescribed for nearly as many actual or imaginary ills.

There is even a fairly authentic rumor that a Welsh physician a hundred years before Withering knew that the foxglove was useful for dropsy, and Withering knew that the plant was also an old wives' remedy for dropsy in Yorkshire. In fact, he ran across "a traveling Yorkshire tradesman" who was vomiting, his vision indistinct and his pulse "forty to the minute," because his wife made him drink a too-concentrated brew of foxglove leaves. Withering wrote that the tradesman's wife might know the value of the plant for dropsy, "but the good woman knew the medicine of her country, but not the dose of it, for her husband narrowly escaped with his life."

The foxglove, in other words, was a potentially dangerous plant, and Withering set about the job of finding what its true uses were, what part of the plant was active, and what was the proper dosage for dropsy. There was then no true answer to such questions, and it took him ten years before he was able to answer them in a book that is today a medical classic.

Linnaeus, in 1753, had adopted Fuch's name for the foxglove, *Digitalis purpurea,* and this name it has held ever since. It belongs to a family of plants containing some poisonous herbs, and Withering moved with extreme caution. *Digitalis* being a biennial, whose root system is sparse, he excluded the roots, and finally the flowers and the seeds. Ultimately he was convinced that the cure resided only in the leaves, picked when the plant is in full flower, *i.e.,* in the second and final year of the plant's life.

By trials on some dropsical charity patients he also found that in using foxglove leaves, he must discard the midrib and the leaf stalk, for it is only in the blade of the leaf that the active principle is concentrated. But how to keep fresh leaves, or, if they were needed in the future, how to dry them properly, and most important of all, what was the safe dosage?

He tried measured doses of the fresh leaves in infusious or tinctures, but ultimately discarded such liquid applications for the dried leaf. He was at that time living in something close to a mansion in the heart of Birmingham. His income had become very large, for he was reputed to have a more lucrative practice than any other doctor in the Midlands, and some thought more than his Harley Street colleagues. But neither riches nor fame nor membership in the Lunar Society could divert him from solving the *Digitalis* puzzle.

In drying foxglove leaves, he would at first trust no one. Sitting in front of a fire in his study, he held over the coals a frying pan with a few fresh leaves. These he slowly dried out so that "when rubbed between finger and thumb" they became a fine powder easily. This was the origin of digitalis as a drug, and even today many doctors prefer this dried leaf powder of digitalis to some of its derivatives.

When he had solved the drying technique, the next step was how much of this powder was safe, how little could he give to be effective, and how long could he continue to use it—in other words, were its effects cumulative and how long did it remain in the patient's body? All of these were distinctly troublesome questions. In the first place, there were not too many dropsical patients, and some of these were practically moribund. There was, too, the obvious overdosage of the old Shropshire woman and of the "traveling trades-man" of Yorkshire.

In such overdoses, digitalis always causes severe nausea, purging and vomiting, and its effectiveness in curing dropsy is nullified. After innumerable trials, Withering finally settled on a dosage. "I give to adults from one to three grains of this powder twice a day. In the reduced state in which physicians generally find dropsical patients, four grains a day are sufficient." Today the dosage of digitalis, after nearly two hundred years, is not very different.

Such was the skill and acumen of Withering that Goodman and Gilman's monumental *The Pharmacological Basis of Therapeutics* warns modern doctors that "Every physician who uses digitalis would do well to read this scholarly work because many of the common errors current in digitalis medication were clearly anticipated and warned against by Withering."

An Account of the Foxglove and some of its Medical Uses with Practical Remarks on Dropsy and other Diseases was published in 1785. It is this book by Withering that has become not only a medical classic but has pointed the way for digitalis to become a life-saving drug ever since. It took him ten years to accumulate the data, and, like any first-class scientist, he reported not only his successes but the failures.

Dropsy is characterized by an unwanted accumulation of liquid in body cavities such as the chest and abdomen. It also causes tremendous swelling in the legs and ankles. The powdered leaves of the foxglove usually result in a dramatic reduction in this misplaced liquid, and in a short time the patient may become nearly normal. No one then knew that dropsy was not in itself a disease, but only a dreaded manifestation of something else. Withering had at first no suspicion of what the fundamental cause of dropsy could be. All he demonstrated so conclusively was that digitalis reduced the dangerous accumulation of liquid.

The publication of his *Account of the Foxglove* made epoch-making news in England, and Withering even sent seeds of the plant to America. All the physicians in the Midlands and many in London knew that Withering had been working on the dropsy-digitalis problem for years before he was ready to publish his results in 1785. No one suspected that its publication would touch off another scandal to shock Withering and his colleagues, or that its instigator was the same man who later attempted to smirch Withering's *Botanical Arrangement*.

On January 14, 1785, Dr. Erasmus Darwin read a paper on the use of digitalis in dropsy, and it was published in the local medical transactions. Every doctor in Birmingham knew that Darwin first learned of digitalis from Withering. But his antipathy to Withering and his desire to be the first doctor to print an account of the plant led him into a disgraceful attempt at priority stealing. His paper appeared a short time before Withering's book, but Darwin did not mention Withering's name or credit him with the discovery. One later commentator characterized Darwin's action as that of an "unethical priority grabber."

The medical profession and the learned world of England were quick to shower honors on Withering. Ultimately he was elected to membership in the Royal Society and to the Linnaean Society of London; other honors came from France and Germany. One French botanist named a genus of tropical American plants *Witheringia* in his honor.

Even the publication of epoch-making books, one on botany and the other on medicine, did not exhaust the abounding intellectual drive of Withering. He wrote books, pamphlets or reviews on subjects that interested him, such as chemistry, meteorology, water analysis, flora of Portugal and the antiquities at Stonehenge. Ultimately failing health and the smoky grime of a Birmingham winter drove him to Portugal for two seasons. He had already rented Edgbaston Hall, a mansion with considerable acreage on the outskirts of the city, where he wrote and carried on breeding experiments with

Guernsey, Jersey and other milk cattle. Apparently this was scarcely a profitable venture, and he wrote to a friend a sentence that still rings true for all so-called gentlemen farmers:

Persons of genius never become rich by farming; such schemes of economy will always render their professors poor.

It was while he rented Edgbaston Hall, now in a delightful suburb of Birmingham, that he nearly lost it in the riots of 1791. Several members of the Lunar Society and scores of liberal-minded citizens decided to give a dinner on the first anniversary of Bastille Day to "commemorate the auspicious day which witnessed the emancipation of twenty-six millions of people from the yoke of despotism."

The French Revolution was by no means popular among all the people in England, who saw in it a threat to the monarchy—perhaps the obliteration of the Lords, the Commons and even the Church. Whatever the cause, the dinner in Birmingham touched off riots that lasted three days. Many houses and dissenting chapels were burned, and some of the drunken rioters perished in the flames they started. A particularly outrageous case was the burning of the house, library, laboratory and scientific records of Dr. Joseph Priestley, who, with his family, barely escaped with their lives.

Withering, playing for time, saved Edgbaston Hall only after some brisk fighting, which ended with the arrival of troops, and in a few days Birmingham was in the hands of the proper authorities. But failing health and the responsibilities of such a big mansion as Edgbaston, where he could no longer walk up stairs, convinced Withering that he should give it up. He bought "The Larches," began improving it and finally moved into it only nine days before his death—from tuberculosis. A day or two before he died, a friend who had just left him said, "The flower of English physicians is indeed Withering."

He died on October 6, 1799, and was buried in a vault in Edgbaston Old Church (St. Bartholomew's) amid the sorrow and adulation of distinguished mourners. A recent visit to the Old Church, which is close to Edgbaston Hall, discloses a beautiful rural edifice, originally founded in 1340, although there may have been a Christian church there as early as A.D. 796. Today its aura of sanctity, its mellowed stained-glass windows and its memorials to past parishioners give it an atmosphere unique among rural churches. Suffusing a faint glow, there burns a bronze sanctuary lamp which scarcely lights the dim interior, on one wall of which is a black marble tablet. See the illustration following page 134.

As the illustration shows, there is chiseled in the marble at the right a sprig of *Digitalis purpurea,* and on the left a piece of *Witheringia,* the plant named for him by L'Heritier de Brutelle.

The Great Medical Mistake

Every doctor in the last years of the eighteenth century believed that dropsy was a disease and that Withering had found the cure for it in the leaves of the foxglove (*Digitalis purpurea*). But sometime before his death, he had an inkling that perhaps digitalis had more important uses. The stethoscope was not invented by René Laënnec, a French physician, until twenty years after Withering's death. Without it, there were only the crudest methods for gauging the activity of the heart. But in spite of this lack, Withering wrote:

That it [digitalis] has a power over the motion of the heart, to a degree yet unobserved in any other medicine, and that this power may be converted to Salutary ends.

If the British are masters of understatement, this tentative guess of Withering's should get some sort of a prize! For digitalis is now a world remedy for what modern doctors call congestive heart failure and others call the failing heart. But in the closing years of the eighteenth century, no one knew that dropsy was usually nothing but a symptom of heart disease. Every doctor thought that digitalis forced great quantities of water from bodies drowned in it, because of the action on the kidneys. But they were wrong, and the diuretic effects of foxglove leaves were only incidental.

Giving digitalis leaves to patients with dropsy was actually curing an unsuspected condition of the heart. In other words, eighteenth-century doctors were curing or helping heart disease without the least idea they were doing so. All they were doing was congratulating themselves for Withering's having found a way to remedy nearly all cases of dropsy.

Not quite all of them, however, and it was some years later that it was proved that all dropsies not caused by heart disease were completely immune to digitalis. In other words, the drug was not a diuretic, but *the* drug to regulate the failing heart. That is its great use today, and untold millions of lives have been saved by it, or, at least, the victims are able to lead reasonably normal lives by regulated maintenance doses of digitalis or its derivatives.

Dropsy is now rare, for all cases due to heart disease are controlled by the digitalis given for the regulation of the failing heart. But the rise to fame of digitalis as *the* drug for congestive heart failure was by no means rapid. For years there was considerable fumbling, most of it consisting of doing things that Whithering had warned against. Also, there was a good bit of fear involved, for even moderate overdosing produced alarming results, and heavy doses were quickly fatal. Many tentative techniques were suggested—all seeking to solve the riddle of the unknown toxicity of a drug powerful, dangerous and potentially life-saving.

No one dared experiment on human beings, and the problem was complicated because the scientists had at least two other drugs which they wanted to compare with digitalis. One of them was the dried skin of an Asiatic toad, which the Chinese had known for centuries. Toad skins were also known to some Amazonian Indians as useful for tipping poisoned arrows. The Asiatic toad and even its English prototype were found to have digitalis-like effects on the failing heart.

The other possible substitute for digitalis was the dried inner scales of the bulb of the sea onion (*Urginea martima*), a bulbous squill from the Mediterranean region well known to the Egyptians as early as 1500 B.C. The Romans used it as a diuretic and what they called a "heart tonic," which came close to its digitalis-like properties.

One of the brilliant successes of science was solving the toxicity of such drugs, for all of them are dangerous. Allied to this problem was finding out what was a safe and effective dose, long before the invention of the electrocardiograph. Before the use of that instrument, the only way to test the value or dangers of a heart drug was by experiments on animals. The two most used were the heart of a frog and a cat. Gradually, digitalis became standardized by what were known as cat units—the amount of digitalis it took to kill a cat. After years of experiment a safe and effective dosage for humans was evolved without killing any more cats.

All of this work was done with the powdered leaves of the foxglove, and the United States *Pharmacopœia* still says that the drug must be "the dried leaf of *Digitalis purpurea*," which is precisely what Withering said about it nearly two hundred years ago. It is today dispensed in capsules or pills, except for those who can swallow neither, for whom liquid preparations are available.

In spite of years of effort by a battery of organic chemists who have given us many laboratory-inspired drugs, digitalis has never been made synthetically. It is thus, after volumes of work on it, and after all these years, a purely natural product. Only its culture, drying and preparation have improved since Withering's day.

Two things about it always puzzled the early workers. One was what, exactly, was its action on the heart? In other words, what was the mechanism of its action? How could such a potentially dangerous drug confine itself to a single organ of the body, with negligible effects elsewhere? If such questions seemed baffling in the nineteenth century, they still are, for no answer is available.

The other question was actually far more complicated. It had always been suspected that the leaf of the foxglove contained one or two, and maybe more, active principles. And it was surmised that these hypothetical ingredients were, in fact, *the* reason that digitalis was so effective. The hunt for such elusive pyxies had been going on for years, but finally, in 1869, Nativelle, a French chemist, isolated what has been known since as *digitoxin*.

This ingredient of digitalis is far more powerful and much more dangerous than the crude leaf. Many doctors use it because it acts much more quickly than digitalis, but they heed well the warning *"Digitoxin is extremely poisonous."* So true is this that the dosage of digitoxin may be as little as 1/350 of a grain, as a maintenance dose, more rarely as much as 1/90 of a grain when emergencies demand it. Digitalis, in comparison, is often given in doses of 10-20 grains within thirty-six to forty-eight hours.

Several other substances have since been isolated from digitalis leaves, but these are of interest only to specialists. The result of all these studies provided the average physician with two superlative drugs for the failing heart, derived from the foxglove—digitalis and digitoxin—leaving to the cardiologist the more unusual ingredients of this magical leaf. Today thousands of doctors all over the world are using these precious life-saving gifts of Nature, uncovered by the ingenuity of man.

Twenty years after Withering's death, a minor British poet was wandering rather aimlessly over central Europe. He was also a physician and on the edge of vagrancy, hence far removed from the men who made digitalis what it is. But one of his poems contains a line that should perhaps hang in the office of every cardiologist, "Wilt thou Cure thine Heart?" That is what grateful physicians are doing with a leaf found for them by a Birmingham doctor and a Shropshire farm woman who told him "foxglove is good for dropsy."

Source of atropine, a doctor's standby

9. The Potato's Lethal Cousins

Give me to drink mandragora
That I might sleep out this great gap of time.
—*Antony and Cleopatra*

In the dining room of the eighteenth-century Washington Hotel in Princess Anne, Maryland, there hung for many years a pictorial plate, now in the writer's study. It depicts an incident in the history of France and illustrates the superstition that the potato was poisonous.

When this tuber first came from Peru to Europe, there was violent opposition to it upon the completely erroneous notion that it was as dangerous as the mandrake of Shakespeare.

The King of France was determined to break down this superstition and invited the aristocracy of Paris and such savants as Lavoisier and Benjamin Franklin to a sumptuous but all-potato dinner. Marie Antoinette even wore its blossoms in her hair. But such lavish sponsorship of the spud failed to overcome the peasants' opposition to it, and the King then had an idea typically French.

On the outskirts of Paris, he planted a potato field and put a troop of soldiers to guard it all day. He figured the peasants would think such royal precautions would be taken only for something of great value. He withdrew the guard at night and royal surmises proved correct, for the peasants began nocturnal stealing of what they had previously scorned.

The pictorial plate labeled "Le cercle des pommes de terre" shows a group of eighteenth-century, gaily uniformed soldiers standing around a basket of potatoes apparently just harvested. Nothing could so well whet the cupidity of the peasants, and night after night they depleted the field. The King literally invited the thefts that ultimately spread the potato all over France.

While the potato is, of course, quite harmless, many of its cousins are far from that. They all belong to a huge family of plants comprising perhaps eighty genera and about three thousand species of herbs, vines, shrubs and trees, many of them tropical. It is a strikingly diverse family, called the Solanaceae by the botanists, and contains, besides the potato, the eggplant, tomato, green and red peppers, and many garden ornamentals like the petunia, salpiglossis and the ghostly angel's trumpet of Peru.

But the superstition of European peasants in the seventeenth and eighteenth centuries had some basis, rooted in a traditional suspicion that *any* plant of the Solanaceae might be dangerous. They all knew of the recently introduced tobacco from the New World. And there had trickled down the centuries the legends of the dreaded mandrake, of the bizarre visions induced by datura, of the deadly nightshade and the equally lethal henbane, not to speak of the use of belladonna to brighten the eyes of Italian ladies. All of these plants belong to the potato family (Solanaceae).

SACRED
TO THE MEMORY OF
WILLIAM WITHERING, M.D., F.R.S.
(etc. etc.)
WHO WAS BORN ON MARCH 28, 1741,
AND DIED OCTOBER 6, 1799,
AGED 58 YEARS

While heav'n-born Genius drops on earth a tear,
And Science, drooping, mourns o'er Withering's bier;
While Pity sighs to find that bosom cold,
Where late she reign'd, dispensing good untold;
While Memory's voice, each virtue telling o'er,
But deeper wounds the peace she would restore,
Hope smiles serene—her eye upturn'd to Heav'n
Where Virtue's never-fading crown is giv'n,
Sheds o'er the weeping sorrowers below
That calm a Christian's grief alone can know.
Yes! on that day, when Nature's ruin'd frame
Shall form a grave for each illustrious name,
And Science' star, on earth so seeming bright,
Shall be eclips'd in universal light,
Then shall the sainted sage that bliss receive,
Which here no tongue can paint, no heart conceive,
While Angel choirs, with plaudits justly given,
Proclaim his triumphs to the hosts of Heav'n.

SACRED
TO THE MEMORY OF
WILL.M WITHERING, M.D. F.R.S.
&c &c
WHO WAS BORN MARCH 28TH 1741.
AND DIED OCT. 6TH 1799.
AGED 58 YEARS.

While heav'n born Genius drops on earth a tear,
And Science, drooping mourns o'er Withering's bier;
While Pity sighs to find that bosom cold
Where late she reign'd, dispensing good untold;
While Memory's voice, each virtue telling o'er,
But deeper wounds the peace she would restore;
Hope smiles serene, her eye upturn'd to Heav'n,
Where Virtue's never-fading crown is giv'n,
Sheds o'er the weeping sorrowers below,
That calm a Christian's grief alone can know.
Yes! on that day, when Nature's ruin'd frame
Shall form a grave for each illustrious name,
And Science' star, on earth so seeming bright,
Shall be eclips'd in universal light,
Then shall the sainted sage that bliss receive,
Which here no tongue can paint, no heart conceive;
While Angel choirs, with plaudits justly giv'n,
Proclaim his triumph to the hosts of Heav'n.

What they did not know then, and has only been discovered within the last century or so, is that some of these dread potions of the Solanaceae contain extremely valuable, but potentially hazardous, drugs. These are used today by modern doctors for a variety of diseases, but only with extreme caution. One of them, for instance, is prescribed in dosages as small as 1/120 of a grain. The ordinary aspirin pill is 5 grains.

These valuable constituents are mostly *alkaloids,* a term that it is practically impossible to define in plain English: familiar examples are quinine, caffeine and cocaine. There are hundreds of others found in many plants that are not even related to the Solanaceae. To the organic chemist and to other specialists alkaloids are a commonplace, but for most of us they remain somewhat esoteric substances that have been isolated from plants.

Alkaloids are, in fact, the active constituents of many drug plants, the crude infusions or extracts of which have been known for hundreds, and in some cases thousands, of years. The ancients found, when or where it is often impossible to tell, that these crude drugs had certain useful properties, without a suspicion that their value rested in their alkaloidal content. They should scarcely be charged with ignorance, for the first alkaloid was not isolated until early in the nineteenth century.

The alkaloids of the potato family often perpetuate and quite certainly potentiate the effects of the simple potions of the ancients. Who among those early herb doctors ever suspected that their crude infusions would point the way to a product that is in every doctor's battery of life-saving drugs? Or that another potion would ever become the drug used in the once popular "twilight sleep," or help the squeamish to forget seasickness?

Superstition and terror, mixed with a large dose of magical hocus-pocus, infuse the history of these ancient nostrums.

Some were obviously beneficial. But others exist chiefly in the annals of crime—murder, theft, prostitution and the nefarious white slave traffic. Such is the remarkable property of a few of them that the victim of a crime, perpetrated under their influence, loses all memory of the event. Every doctor knows the value of this memory loss, as do those who treat the mentally disturbed, or a man in delirium tremens, or those in maniacal states.

One of the most ancient and notorious of these plants of the potato family is the legendary mandrake. Cursed by many, sought by multitudes of women, it had the distinction of having made surgical operations possible two thousand years before the discovery of ether.

Mandrake (*Mandragora Officinarum*)

Much of the history of the mandrake is unprintable. For this apparently innocent-looking herb of the eastern Mediterranean region has sparked sexual orgies that would bring the blush of shame even to Hollywood. Its carefully censored history is sufficiently bizarre for such a small perennial, stemless plant. Its leaves are all basal, and it ultimately bears a blue, violet or yellowish, cup-shaped, rather small flower. It is neither very striking nor is it much, if ever, grown as an ornamental.

But its virtues do not lie in the vegetative part of the plant but in the root. These are thickish, somewhat tuberous, and forked into two leg-like branches, hence the name mandrake, *i.e.*, a potent male. There grew up a welter of incredible female legends over this morphological accident. If the gods made a plant with what seemed like a heaven-sent likeness to the male, it was but a step to ascribe masculine virility to this magical root.

Incredulous women for hundreds of years collected the

roots, paid high prices for perfect specimens, and hung them from the rafters of their homes throughout the Near East, especially in Palestine. For what barren woman would not eagerly seek such a prize? It was supposed to ensure conception, promote sexual passion, thaw frigid women and was often used in those illicit Roman orgies that defy description.

The plant is not an aphrodisiac, but the incredible persistence of the belief in its magical powers has not yet died. Rather recently, imitation mandrakes, made of gold, silver or pottery, were offered for sale in the Levant, the implication being that the false copy might have the same attributes as the root. Even as late as 1934 the legend lingered. In that year an affluent but childless Jew in the United States, who had helped in the early days of what is now Israel, was sent a mandrake root by the grateful Jews of Palestine, with their best wishes!

Some women thought that the small, berry-like yellow fruit of the mandrake had similar powers. From Arabia came its other name—the devil's-apple. These supposedly provocative delicacies were eagerly eaten because "of their power to excite voluptuous sensations." Even the Bible perpetuated the legend. In the thirtieth chapter of Genesis the childless and barren Rachel begs her happily married sister, "Give me, I pray thee, of thy son's mandrake."

Quite apart from these libidinous fancies, the juice of the root, properly diluted, was used by ancient physicians to deaden pain and produce a dream-like sleep that lasted for hours, and, with heavy doses, for days. It could also kill, for Galen, one old chronicler, warns that it "must be warily used, for it slayeth if men take much thereof."

So well known were its anesthetic properties that Dioscorides, a Greek physician of the first century, wrote that a patient about to be operated upon was given mandrake and became "overborne with dead sleep," so that the surgeon could painlessly "cut or cauterize." Modern experts are a bit skeptical as to its anesthetic value, but its general use by Greek, Roman and Arabian doctors is well authenticated.

Many kind-hearted women in Jerusalem had no doubts about its anesthetic qualities. When the Romans introduced crucifixion into Palestine, these women would offer the victims a sponge soaked in mandrake juice. The criminal would often become insensible, taken for dead by the soldiers, and removed from the cross. So many recovered after a few hours of insensibility that the Roman governors ordered that all bodies, before delivery to waiting relatives, should be mutilated.

The legends, pro and con, lasted for centuries. More than twenty books on the mandrake were issued between 1510 and 1850. Some, like John Gerarde's *Herbal* of 1597, said of the mandrake's properties "that they are all and every part of them false and most untrue." But Hippocrates, a name revered by modern doctors, wrote about 400 B.C. that the mandrake would relieve depression and anxiety. He and the surgeons who used it as an anesthetic were suggesting, without knowing why, that it contained one of those mysterious alkaloids of which they knew nothing.

Today it is in no modern pharmacopœia and hence has no official sanction. Its inclusion here is simply because it points the way to the ultimate and extremely valuable properties of some of its relatives in the potato family. It will scarcely, however, live down its disreputable past, and most think of it as Shakespeare did in Henry IV, when one of his characters was "lecherous as a monkey and the whores called him—mandrake."

Datura (*Datura Stramonium*)

Scarcely any plant of the potato family is so widely distributed as this evil-smelling weed. So rank is its odor that most people avoid it, and children should be warned against nibbling, for its juice and seeds are apt to be fatal. Known for thousands of years in India, where it was probably native, it has spread nearly all over the world.

It perhaps reached North America at Jamestown, Virginia, where the records tell us that some sailors at that early English settlement were poisoned by it. They had ignorantly used it like spinach, with almost fatal results. From that incident the plant became known as Jamestown weed, now shortened to the familiar jimsonweed.

This is a rather handsome annual, three to five feet high, with broad, large leaves and a striking trumpet-shaped flower that may be three to five inches long, generally white (with greenish stripes) or, in a variety, violet or bluish-violet. These are followed by a thorny capsule filled with brownish or darker-colored seeds. Because of the prickly pod the plant is often called thorn apple. All parts of the plant are poisonous, especially the juice and seeds. It grows about dooryards, along roadsides and in fields, thriving on dung heaps and rubbish piles.

Almost no other plant has such a history of crime. In the Middle Ages, especially in Italy, professional poisoners would concoct a brew of *Datura* that would be almost painlessly fatal. That quality of deadening the senses before death, or during the perpetration of a crime, made it of the greatest value to criminals.

So well known was this ability that Christoval Acosta, who was in India in 1578, wrote that Hindu whores gave it to their patrons because "these mundane ladies are such mistresses and adepts in the use of the seed that they gave it in

Stramonium: a valuable drug with an evil history

doses corresponding to as many hours as they wish their poor victims to be unconscious or transported."

Still worse was the use of *Datura Stramonium* by the nefarious white slavers. Virgins who may not have wanted to become prostitutes were given a pleasant-tasting but diabolical brew containing an aphrodisiac and datura. Under the combined influence of these drugs, they actively contributed to the loss of their virginity, but upon subsequent awakening had no memory of their actions. With such an evil background, it is little wonder that the jimsonweed acquired a black reputation.

Notwithstanding its evil repute, the United States annually imports over two hundred thousand pounds of the dried leaf of *stramonium*. This is merely the crude drug, destined to be made up into capsules, tinctures and extracts, now valuable in a variety of diseases. Two where it is especially appreciated are asthma and Parkinson's disease, for while it cures neither, it greatly relieves distressing symptoms.

Datura is not a dope in the ordinary sense of that term. It does not merely put a person to sleep, any more than it did with the girls mentioned above. But it contains one or more of the alkaloids found in many plants of the potato family, which have a unique action on the nervous system and the brain. All the early writers and their modern scientific successors stress the unique quality of these hidden ingredients. One of them writes:

He who partakes of it is deprived of his reason; for a long time laughing or weeping, or sleeping and oftentimes talking and replying, so that at times he appears to be in his right mind, but really being out of it and not knowing to whom he is speaking, *nor remembering what has happened after his alienation has passed.* (Italics the author's)

Such a remarkable quality could not fail to interest the doctors, and since the early part of this century much new light has been directed at these lethal cousins of the potato. *Stramonium* is not the most important of them, even if it is one of the most ancient. Medically it is far surpassed by the plant used by Italian females to brighten their eyes.

Deadly Nightshade (*Atropa Belladonna*)

This perennial herb, the most important drug plant in the potato family, is so poisonous that it was appropriately named for Atropos, that one of the three Fates who cut the thread of life. Years before, Italian ladies had a less drastic name for it which has survived ever since. They found that a dilute drop of the juice put into their eyes greatly expanded the pupil and made their eyes brighten; they promptly named it belladonna, or beautiful lady. Modern opthalmologists still use its active ingredient when they need to expand the pupil. But that is a very minor use of belladonna, which is one of the most widely used of all drugs.

The crude drug and its amazing constituents are all derived from a European and Asiatic plant that grows about two to three feet high, having ovalish leaves about four inches long, arranged alternately and without marginal teeth. The nodding flowers, borne singly or in pairs, are about one inch long, purplish-red, and followed by a blackish sweet berry about half an inch in diameter. All parts of the plant are violently poisonous (not to the touch), and if it is ever cultivated for ornament, which is not advocated, children should be warned to let it alone. A single berry may be fatal. Medieval poisoners knew this so well that belladonna, like its cousins in the potato family, was infamous during the Middle Ages.

Its dangerous juice did not prevent Spanish ladies from making a cosmetic out of its fruit to whiten their complexions. But centuries earlier Locusta, a notorious Roman poisoner, was hired to make away with women who no longer enchanted their husbands or lovers. She also poisoned the Emperor Claudius, and was finally executed in A.D. 68. Belladonna was her poison.

The active constituent of this plant, which Dioscorides knew in the first century, eluded discovery for eighteen hundred years. In 1809 it was isolated, rather crudely, but by 1819 it was definitely proved to be an alkaloid and named *atropine*. Today the *United States Pharmacopœia* says, "*Caution—atropine is extremely poisonous.*" Doctors know this so well that it is prescribed in extremely minute doses, some as small as 1/250 of a grain.

Also it does so many different things to such various parts of our body that the physician may sometimes be in a quandary as to which target will be best worth shooting at. If, for instance, disease A is likely to be cured with atropine, what will be its unwanted effects upon other and completely normal functions? Or, if disease B seems amenable to atropine therapy, will the known toxicity of the drug on some other organ preclude its use altogther? Such questions, and there are many of them, can only be answered by a physician well versed in the alkaloids found in these lethal cousins of the potato.

Very little atropine is found in the leaves of belladonna, which are harvested when the plant is in full flower. A little more is found in its root and in the underground part of a related plant (*Atropa acuminata*) from India. Both plants are Old World in origin and for many years the United States had to import all belladonna leaves and the extracted atropine. But since the end of World War I, and especially since World War II, enterprising botanical drug firms have so perfected its culture that the United States is now actually exporting it to Europe. These belladonna farms are mostly in Pennsylvania, Ohio, Wisconsin and California, especially the latter.

Why we use so much is no mystery to the physician. A recent check of several textbooks on therapy discloses that belladonna (the deadly nightshade) or its derivative atropine is prescribed in over thirty different medical troubles. These range in seriousness from the misery of hay fever to the terrible tremors of paralysis agitans, better known to the laity as shaking palsy or Parkinson's disease.

The bounty of Nature is hardly better illustrated than in the protean benefits of belladonna and atropine. In so many diseases these drugs simply cannot be replaced. If they are today sometimes nudged into oblivion by synthetics, these were all sparked by studying the alkaloids found in these magical relatives of the potato.

No wonder the experts lump them all as "Belladonna Alkaloids" or "Solanaceous drugs." The first reminds us that belladonna is a prime source, and Solanaceous confirms the fact that all of them are confined to the potato family. What Solanaceous does not tell us has been uncovered by the organic chemists. Perhaps these savants listened a little to the legends of the Crucifixion, to the tales of Hindu whores, or even to

the professional poisoners of the Middle Ages. They un-
doubtedly knew of the more reasoned observations of Dioscorides, Pliny and Galen. For all these plants were well
known to the ancients, but until their active constituents
were isolated, there was no safe way of using them.

What the organic chemists discovered was that atropine is
merely one alkaloid found not only in belladonna, but in
several other plants. Could it be possible that there were still
other alkaloids in belladonna? Or in plants related to it? An
enormous amount of fundamental research has since been
lavished on these Solanaceous alkaloids and upon their amazing efficacy in serious diseases. Hardly any other whisper from
the earth is now so loud, but before listening to it, let us look
briefly at other sources of them.

How to Kill an Emu

About 1861 Australians first heard of a plant with rather
remarkable properties that grew in the interior where both
desert and scrub abound. Its leaves, dropped in a water hole,
would bring fish to the surface and kill an almost ostrich-size
bird known as the emu. For centuries the natives had been
using the flesh of such fish and of the emu, both of which
were palatable and safe, regardless of the poisonous method
of getting it.

It soon became clear that the "black fellows" of the interior were chewing a quid of the leaves of this plant as a
narcotic and a stimulant. Its effects are remarkable. They can
go for hours or even days without much food and with very
little water. One of the early Australian expeditions into the
interior first recorded the occurrence of this plant, and since
then it has become of nearly worldwide interest. Known first
as pedeheri, and later by several other names, it has finally
come to us as *pituri*, a purely native product from a region

of Australia which one of their scientists designated as of "expressionless monotony."

Here lived a group of generally naked natives who were as primitive as any on earth. How they found that the leaves of this shrub had such startling effectiveness, no one will ever know. But Australian and ultimately European scientists were eager to explore the qualities of a leaf, the juice of which would stupefy fish and kill an emu without poisoning the flesh of either. This, and its effects on the natives, suggested the idea that the juice of pituri acted directly on the nervous system.

Australian scientists finally pinned the identity of pituri to one or two, or maybe three, shrubs or small trees, ultimately named *Duboisia*. This small group of wholly Australian plants belongs to the potato family, and the scientists were quick to suspect that *Duboisia* might be first cousin to the mandrake, jimsonweed and the deadly nightshade.

Not only is pituri botanically related to these plants, but subsequent investigation disclosed that it contains several of the alkaloids found in the older and better-known sources. So dramatic a discovery finally led to commercial plantations of *Duboisia* and the extraction of at least two of its alkaloids. These are atropine and scopolamine, both of nearly worldwide use.

The discovery of pituri, and what came of it, is thus another whisper from the earth that has become so loud that every doctor must heed it. These "black fellows," searching for something to ease the stress of their incredibly primitive life, inevitably pointed the way for science to ask the imperative "How?" and "Why?" In the course of that work they found not only atropine and scopolamine in *Duboisia* but still another alkaloid hitherto associated with a very different plant.

Henbane (*Hyoscyamus niger*)

This Eurasian herb does not grow higher than two feet in its annual form, but the biennial plant may be twice as high. Only its leaves and flowering tops are of any medicinal value, and they have been collected for over two thousand years, both as a medicine and as a poison. Many years ago it was introduced, probably inadvertently, into the United States and Canada, where it chiefly inhabits waste places and roadsides as a rather dangerous and evil-smelling weed.

Henbane would be of no interest if it did not contain at least two alkaloids of the potato family—one of them of supreme importance. This is scopolamine; the other is hyoscyamine. The latter is little used in medicine, but it is of paramount importance because of its convertibility into atropine. Henbane is now grown commercially in the United States, largely as a source of atropine.

That henbane harbored potent extracts was well known to Pliny, who wrote in A.D. 60:

For this is certainly known, that, if one take it in drink more than four leaves, it will put him beside himself.

Such a quality was esteemed by criminals who used henbane, in somewhat stronger concentrations, to make "knock-out drops," especially in the Middle Ages. The plant is, of course, poisonous, and its yellowish, purple-striped flowers are scarcely worth cultivating for ornament. It should be avoided by children, although its rank odor scarcely encourages handling.

No attribute of Nature is so complicated as her scattering of these potent alkaloids among half a dozen relatives of the potato. The chemistry of them baffled the scientists for years. Their uses in medicine are hazardous enough to warrant extreme caution, and their early and bizarre history is inextricably linked to crime. Today these varied products provide us with drugs that have such wide use that volumes are written about them by medical experts.

To untangle this complexity is beyond the scope of this book, and perhaps beyond the patience of the reader. But a simple tabulation of the plants involved and the alkaloids found in them may prove helpful in an appraisal of their extraordinary properties.

They are arranged in the order of their treatment earlier in this chapter, and it is apparent that some plants are far more productive of alkaloids than others. But they are sufficiently alike so that the experts lump them as "Belladonna Alkaloids."

CHIEF SOURCES OF THE BELLADONNA ALKALOIDS

Mandrake (*Mandragora officinarum*).

This ancient anesthetic probably contains *atropine, hyoscyamine* and *scopolamine*. It is completely obsolete in modern medicine.

Datura (*Datura Stramonium*).

The familiar jimsonweed is a valuable source of *hyoscyamine, atropine* and *scopolamine*.

Deadly nightshade (*Atropa Belladonna*).

A poisonous herb that yields both *atropine* and *scopolamine*.

Pituri (*Duboisia,* probably two species).

Australian shrubs and trees, the leaves of which are rich in *scopolamine*.

Henbane (*Hyoscyamus niger*)

A stinking Eurasian herb which yields *hyoscyamine, scopolamine* and *atropine*.

Scopola * (*Scopolia carniolica*)

Yields *hyoscyamine* and *scopolamine*.

---

* Not treated above, this relative of the deadly nightshade is a minor source of alkaloids.

A brief summary of this makes it fairly clear that only three of the alkaloids are found in several different plants. Of these three only two are of prime importance in medicine today. In the approximate order of importance, these three are:

Atropine. Found in datura, atropa and henbane.
Scopolamine. Found in datura, atropa, *Duboisia,* henbane and scopola.
Hyoscyamine. Found in datura, henbane and scopola.

Besides these three, a score of other alkaloids have been isolated from these plants, but they are of minor interest. And of the three, *atropine* and *scopolamine* are far more important than *hyoscyamine,* which has a much more limited use.

Prescriptions, and even drugstore nostrums, that contain atropine and scopolamine are so legion that only a glimpse of their varied use can be noted here. Both alkaloids are so dangerous that their dosage varies generally between 1/500 to 1/100 of a grain, and the *United States Pharmacopœia* warns that both are "extremely poisonous." Such warnings are well heeded by the physician, but such is the value of both drugs that modern medicine might be crippled without them. Synthetic substitutes have been devised, but Goodman and Gilman, in their *Pharmacological Basis of Therapeutics,* write, "The synthetic chemist has not greatly improved upon the products of nature in this field; although a few related derivatives have been introduced into medicine, they do not possess the wide range of therapeutic usefulness which characterizes the naturally occurring belladonna alkaloids."

"WOMEN WERE CONDEMNED BY DIVINE COMMAND TO BRING FORTH IN SORROW"

Thus fulminated a prelate in the medieval town of Freiburg in 1905 when Dr. Carl J. Gauss thought that the pains of labor were cruel, not completely necessary, perhaps because he had a method of easing them. The old routine of giving morphine to women in labor had many disadvantages, and he had the idea that administration of scopolamine with a smaller dose of morphine might be effective in making the birth easier and also have an entirely separate effect. To Dr. Gauss the latter was paramount.

The records do not tell us if he knew of the ancient criminal use of datura by the Hindu whores, the white slavers or the medieval poisoners. But the doctor emphatically did know that scolopamine had an effect on the brain and nervous system so that a patient under its influence could cooperate in producing the baby but lose all recollection of the ordeal. To express this peculiar state of clouded consciousness and comparatively painless birth, he coined the term "Dammerschlaf," which millions of women knew as "twilight sleep." It was not without danger, and has since been replaced by other techniques.

But the significant sequel of Dr. Gauss's idea was not the ultimate abandonment of twilight sleep. He dramatized, in spite of the clergy, that pain and the memory of it could be practically abolished by the selective action of scopolamine. He wrote: "Scopolamine has a direct effect upon the nervous system and the brain, causing by its action an interruption in the mental associations or memory."

Much more simple-minded and far less humane people than Dr. Gauss had known this for centuries, merely by the use of crude extractions from these plants. But here, using a potentially dangerous alkaloid in minute doses, a doctor had demonstrated the amazingly complicated action of this priceless drug.

Such a discovery naturally prompted a spate of research to answer questions that clamored for solution. What, for instance, might be other and valuable uses for scopolamine and its closely related atropine? It soon became evident that the action of these belladonna alkaloids was at least twofold. They had what the doctors called a "blocking action" on the nerves that control many organs. They are also useful for increasing the heart rate, decreasing blood pressure, controlling the violent spasms of asthma and whooping cough, although they cure none of these diseases. So far as the touring public is concerned, scopolamine regulates or abolishes the mechanism that causes seasickness, as well as car and air sickness. It is today the best of all drugs for these harassing afflictions. This benefit was scarcely known before World War II, when thousands of soldiers were landed in Europe, free of the debility following seasickness.

The other effects of atropine and scopolamine upon the nervous system and brain are too numerous to include here. But in one of them they give dramatic relief. Patients suffering from Parkinson's disease have distressing symptoms such as a crippling tremor of the hands, muscular rigidity, abnormal gait, speech difficulties, and a number of other impairments. Fairly large doses of scopolamine, almost in toxic amounts, give welcome but unhappily only temporary relief. It or atropine acts on the brain and nerves, so that the patient's mental outlook is vastly improved.

Another extremely valuable attribute of scopolamine is evidenced in patients who are restless or agitated. Those in delirium tremens, in various psychotic states, some even maniacal, and those who suffer from the agonizing symptoms of the withdrawal of alcohol or narcotics—all these and several others are given scopolamine. Again it works its magical hypnotic and tranquilizing effects, without the patient having an appalling memory of his misery.

Perhaps more important is its use on patients about to endure surgery. Some time before the operation they are often given a hypodermic containing scopolamine and morphine. This helps to reduce the dose of the main anesthetic, and it does much more. Its hypnotic and tranquilizing effect is so welcomed by a possibly apprehensive patient that one of them said, "I hardly knew when I left my bed."

Both atropine and scopolamine also produce an entirely different set of reactions. A single drop of a solution as weak as only one part of the drug to one hundred parts of water will dilate the pupil of the eye in a few minutes. This is sometimes essential to the ophthalmologist, who in certain cases may prolong the dilation for a few days. Atropine or scopolamine will accomplish this, but is now largely replaced by a synthetic that is closely related to atropine.

Another feature of both drugs, especially atropine, is its ability to dry up ordinarily moist surfaces such as the tongue, nasal passages and the upper part of the throat. This is so marked that advantage is taken of it in treating hay fever, asthma and related troubles, including the common cold. This drying effect has been known for centuries before the alkaloids were isolated, and it has to be watched while treating other diseases with atropine. The dry skin, parched mouth and the consequent rise in body temperature may be alarming, but subside when corrected. Sometimes it is so pronounced that patients have a high color, or even a rash, and may be suspected of having scarlet fever.

The few uses cited above give only a glimpse of the real value of these ancient and magical cousins of the potato. Only a medical textbook can do full justice to them. A casual glance at such books reveals that atropine especially and scopolamine a little less so are prescribed in nearly fifty distinct diseases. This is quite a record from the days of Hippocrates, who wrote of one of them in the fourth century B.C.:

A small dose in wine, less than would occasion delirium, will relieve the deepest depression and anxiety.

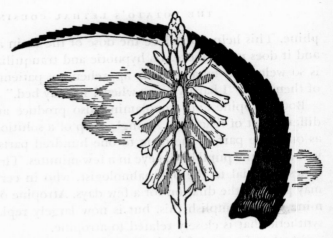

Bitter aloes, one of the oldest cathartics

10. The Cathartic Racket

The triad of the careless routinistic doctor, the "counter-prescribing druggist" and . . . the proprietary pill promoter is responsible for having made a large number of persons "colonic cripples," lifelong slaves to pills.—*Dr. Bernard Fantus.*

THE PUBLIC APPEARS to ignore the learned doctor and hosts of his colleagues. One of the most distinguished, as late as 1961, wrote that many of us suffer from "the fatuous conviction that the body must rid itself of fecal residues in a stereotyped way and very frequently," *i.e.*, at least once a day. This widespread delusion has persisted for well over three thousand years. Herodotus reported about 500 B.C. that the Egyptians "purge themselves every month, three days successively, seeking to preserve health by emetics and enemas, for they suppose that all diseases . . . proceed from the food they use."

Even the witty and brilliant Alexander the Great, on his way to the conquest of Persia and India about 325 B.C., sent a committee to look into the production of one of the most violent of all the plant purges, which throve and still thrives on the island of Socotra, south of Arabia and about five hundred miles east of the African coast. And in many other lands various plants have been discovered by people far less sophisticated than Alexander, all of whom sought relief from what one doctor has called "imaginary constipation," *i.e.*, people who are morbidly bowel-conscious.

The myth of "once a day" is the cause of the astounding statement of the United States Public Health Service that there are six hundred seventy-eight nationally advertised cathartics on sale in the United States. Proportionally England and Germany appear to be suffering just as acutely from this imaginary constipation. Sales of these products total hundreds of millions of dollars annually, much of it quite unnecessary. True constipation, as distinguished from that of the pill-taking, morbidly bowel-conscious multitude, is a quite definite infirmity to be diagnosed and corrected only by a physician.

If he is wise and experienced, he may confine his cure to a regime of proper diet and a reasonable amount of exercise. But sometimes he will have to prescribe drugs, and many of these have been derived from plants. At first, reports about them were quite faint whispers from the earth. But today they are potent drugs that are standard in medical practice and also make up a huge part of the drugstore nostrums.

One of the earliest records of a cathartic was uncovered by Georg Moritz Ebers, a German Egyptologist, in 1872. What has since been called the *Ebers Papyrus* was bought from an Arab at Luxor, who claimed it came from between the knees of a mummy at Thebes. It is actually a medical treatise and deals with the use of over eighteen plant drugs that, three thousand years later, are in the *United States Pharmacopœia*. Among them is the same violent purge that interested Alexander the Great. That superb conqueror wanted to know more about the mysterious plant from Socotra. It had evidently been known in Egypt for twelve hundred years before Alexander's time, and probably for centuries before 1552 B.C., which is the date ascribed to the *Ebers Papyrus*.

That remarkable document lists three standard cathartics: senna, castor oil and aloes, all sufficiently well known at that time to be included in what is one of the earliest of medical texts. All of them grew in Egypt, on Socotra or along the African coast of the Mediterranean, and some of them are now grown all over the world.

While the *Ebers Papyrus* is thus one of the most precious of ancient medical treatises, it failed to mention the tremendous use of Chinese rhubarb, which is far older than any cathartic plant listed in the papyrus. And, of course, it said nothing of American cathartics, which were not known until years after the Spaniards reached the New World.

The term *cathartic* is but a generic name, a catchall for any product that "purifies," which was the initial meaning of *catharsis*. The medicos are never satisfied with such broad generalizations and invented a simple system for distinguishing the actions of the different plants.

Even the layman knows that a *purge* may be drastic, often quickly so, and more or less violent, like the aloes from Socotra. Such a drug suggested to Dr. Oliver Wendell Holmes that "If it were known that a prize fighter were to have a drastic purgative administered two or three days before a contest, no one would question that it would affect the betting on his side unfavorably."

A *laxative* is an agent that is incapable of causing active purgation, no matter what the dose. Mineral oils and olive oil are common examples. So is the popular psyllium seed.

Among the purges, besides the aloe, are castor oil, rhubarb, senna and a few others, divided upon the severity of their action, one of the mildest being jalap from tropical America. None of these purges would ever be called an *aperient,* which is only a mild laxative. By far the oldest of all the cathartics, and still widely used, is one assumed to have been known in China 4,700 years ago.

Rhubarb

Shen Nung, an actual or merely legendary emperor of China, was far more than a beneficent ruler, for he taught a fairly primitive people the use of agricultural implements. He also studied the native flora, and these studies are assumed to have resulted in what amounts to the earliest-known pharmacopoeia, ascribed to the year 2700 B.C.

In it the Emperor lists rhubarb, mahuang, and many other medicinal plants. Modern research has engendered a little doubt as to the accomplishments or even the existence of this powerful and scholarly emperor, who has been called, "the father of Chinese agriculture and medicine." Whether he existed or not, his book, now called *Pen Tsao Kang Mu,* originally listed three hundred sixty-five plants of actual or supposed medicinal value. The Chinese thought so much of this first pharmacopoeia that new editions were ordered in the Han dynasty (A.D. 25-219), again between A.D. 502 and 556, in the Tang dynasty (A.D. 618-905) and a last edition, which is still in print, under the Ming dynasty in 1596.

All of these mentioned rhubarb, which has a history of probably five thousand years of use as a valued cathartic. But it is not the rhubarb of our gardens, the succulent stalks of which most of use eat in the spring upon the completely erroneous notion that it is a mild laxative. Garden rhubarb contains no medicinal properties of any kind beyond a slight admixture of malic and oxalic acid, which gives it crispness and taste. But this juice and delicious flavor are of no cathartic value.

The rhubarb of China would never have persisted for over five thousand years if it contained only the succulence and flavor of garden rhubarb. The stalks of the Chinese plant are never used, as only the underground parts of the plant have any medicinal value. When these roots first became available in Europe, they were very expensive. In France, in 1542, Chinese rhubarb was worth ten times the price of cinnamon.

Even as early as 114 B.C., caravans were taking Chinese rhubarb from Shenski to Bokhara, in what is now Russian territory. And Marco Polo mentions that in the province of Tangut, in extreme northwestern Tibet and adjoining China, rhubarb was produced "in large quantities and the merchants who came to buy it convey it to all parts of the world." This was around the end of the thirteenth century.

Hence it is no surprise that the literature on such a valuable plant is very extensive. It fills volumes, but the essentials are not very complicated, as they all hinge on the identity of a few Chinese and Indian relatives of our common garden rhubarb. All of them belong to what the botanists have christened as *Rheum,* a genus of plants comprising perhaps fifty different species, nearly all of them Asiatic, including our garden variety.

All the rheums are rather coarse plants with broad, long-stalked leaves, small, greenish-white flowers and a large root. All of the fifty species of *Rheum* are ignored except three or four, the roots of which have been harvested and prepared for market for fifty centuries by patient and quite skillful Chinese. Since the last war, some medicinal rhubarb has come also from India and some at least has been exported through India.

No one will ever know how the Chinese first discovered

the properties of these three or four species of *Rheum*. Scattered throughout the mountainous part of western China, in Tibet and in the Himalayas are many worthless kinds, but those that are cathartics of worldwide use today are the only ones that contain the active constituent. This is a resin called *emodin*, which took its name from Mt. Emodus in the Himalayas, where there grew a species called *Rheum emodi*. Emodin has since been found in several other cathartic plants that have nothing to do with rhubarb. Other rhubarbs that contain emodin are *Rheum officinale* from Tibet and *Rheum palmatum* from China, with its variety *tanguticum*, which grows in the region visited by Marco Polo.

These plants are now cultivated on a large scale in China, Tibet and less so in the Himalayas. The plants look not unlike our garden rhubarb, but some of them grow considerably taller, *Rheum emodin* often reaching a height of six to ten feet. The roots are collected only from plants that are six to eight years old, and after digging, the root bark is discarded and the root is washed, split and thoroughly dried. This is the commercial product known as Chinese rhubarb. As received in the drug markets of Europe or the United States, the pieces of root are from two and a half to eight inches long, usually yellowish-brown.

Besides emodin, the medicinal rhubarbs contain an astringent, which induced one expert to call rhubarb the "constipating purge." Emodin works usually only on the contents of the colon, without too much pain or griping, but the astringent often brings on a drug-induced constipation. Hence rhubarb should be used only on the advice of a physician, in spite of the wide lay use of it in various proprietary remedies.

Rhubarb is considered one of the best of the relatively mild purges, and is far less drastic than several others. It is common as a household remedy, mixed with soda and other ingredients.

A Bitter Purge

Just over the border of the French Riviera, near the Italian town of Ventimiglia, lies La Mortola, a superb garden, founded in 1867 by Sir Thomas Hanbury, an affluent Englishman. Besides its enchanting setting, it contains the finest collection of succulent plants in Europe. Among cacti from America, spurges from South Africa and many other drought-resistant succulents, it has one of the best collections in existence of aloes.

These predominantly African ornamentals all belong to the genus *Aloe*, which comprises over two hundred different species, all thick-leaved succulents with enough superficial resemblance to a young century plant often to be mistaken for one.

Some are practically stemless, others have an obvious trunk that may be ten to twenty feet high. All have either a basal or terminal rosette of thirty to forty very thick leaves. These may be two to three inches thick, particularly at the swollen base, are sometimes a yard long, and the spiny-tipped blade is very sharp. Either on the margins or on the surface of the leaf, and sometimes on both, there are several spines or bony teeth, thought by some to arm them against nibbling cattle. The prevailingly yellow or red, slightly curved, tubular flowers are rather showy as they are borne in a terminal cluster.

Many aloes grow wild along the Mediterranean, on the coast of Arabia and one of them on the island of Socotra. The Latin name *Aloe* was derived from *Alloch,* the original Arabian name for one of them.

Aloes are today much cultivated for ornament in southern California, and in many other dryish, frost-free places. But it was not for their beauty that Aristotle suggested to Alexander the Great that he not only look into the production of the drug on Socotra, but conquer that island. On it grew an *Aloe* that produced the most drastic purge known in 325 B.C. It still grows there and from it has come its nearly worldwide culture. This is the origin of bitter aloes, also now derived from at least two other species.

Drug experts still consider Socotrine aloes as superior to the other two. The plant that yields it is *Aloe perryi,* a semi-desert, short-stemmed, red-flowered succulent with leaves spiny only on the margins. It is not cultivated, but there are enough wild plants to make the crude drug the leading industry of this island.

The two other medicinal aloes are grown far from the home of this original species. The so-called West Indian or Curaçao aloes is actually a succulent from the Mediterranean region taken to Barbados around 1690, and subsequently acquiring the name *Aloe barbadensis,* although still called *Aloe vera* by many. It is no longer grown on Barbados, or on Curaçao, being practically a Dutch monopoly on the islands of Aruba and Bonaire.

The third cathartic aloe comes from South Africa, and the natives, especially the Hottentots, appear to have known of it centuries before the first European reached the Cape. Unlike the other two, it has a stem or trunk ten to fifteen feet high and a terminal rosette of thick, spiny leaves. South Africa has perhaps one hundred and thirty different kinds of aloes, but only *Aloe ferox* and one or two relatives are of any interest as cathartics.

The extraction of the drug is essentially a simple but messy process. The active constituent is in the juice of these very fleshy leaves which, like most desert plants, appear to be a little reluctant to release it. The leaves are cut off near the base and often arranged in tiers, with the cut base in a receptacle, often canvas, a goatskin or a wooden trough, and with the leaf tips erect. The slow drainage of the juice may take four or five hours, and the workers well know its intense bitterness against which, and also because of the spines, they wear protective clothing.

When the juice stops draining, it is boiled down to such a consistency that it will solidify when cooled, or in Socotra it is simply air-dried. This hardened mass is the crude aloes of the drug trade, containing the active constituent which, when extracted, is known as aloin. It is the aloin that acts as a relatively strong cathartic and the use of it is so extensive that the United States imports nearly three hundred thousand pounds of the crude aloe in order to extract the needed amount of aloin. The crude bitter aloes is rarely used in prescriptions today, as aloin is used in much smaller doses and is less likely to promote pain and griping.

The clever Dutch on the islands of Aruba and Bonaire have bypassed the messy drainage and boiling down of the juice. There the fresh juice is treated chemically to produce aloin directly, which is shipped as a refined product, thus saving the labor of making crude aloes.

Many people, in nearly every part of the tropical or subtropical world, have used the fresh juice of aloe for a variety of complaints. Its bitter, astringent action is claimed to be effective in skin troubles like eczema, to relieve the pain of burns and more recently to cure X-ray burns, the latter use being quite popular. All such uses are of the fresh juice or pulp of the leaf and have nothing to do with bitter aloes as a fairly drastic cathartic. Many physicians and most of their patients prefer a milder remedy, probably discovered by an Arabian doctor in the ninth century.

An Arabian Benefactor

Baghdad was once the very navel of the Moslem world, a princely city sparkling with fabulous gems, extraordinary rugs and gorgeous mosques, but plagued by fearful summer heat. It had a succession of caliphs, one of the greatest being Harun al-Rashid, who in the ninth century became the hero of many tales in the *Arabian Nights.*

But the opulent splendor of Baghdad scarcely compensated for its lack of good physicians, and Harun invited one of the most famous of Arabian doctors to come to the city, even if the medico was a Nestorian Christian—hence anathema to devout Moslems. The doctor's name was Jahiah-Eben-Masawaih, a trinomial he soon changed to Mesue, and as Mesue the Elder he has come down to us as, next to Avicenna, the greatest of medieval physicians.

His fame rests on many discoveries. One of them, previously unknown, even to the Egyptians, was the first recorded filling of a tooth cavity with gold. But more important was his revolt against a very common medical practice of that day —giving a violent purge to constipated patients. This drastic remedy and its wide use had been suggested by Greek and Roman physicians, and to fly in the face of such traditional experts took courage.

It is now impossible to say that Mesue was the actual discoverer of his proposed alternative, but he was quite certainly the first physician to spread abroad the effectiveness and milder action of the leaves of an Arabian shrub, which has ever since been called senna. In the last ten centuries it has become so popular that the United States annually imports nearly two million pounds of senna leaves, now coming mostly from India. The consumption in Europe is equally impressive.

The source of this fantastically popular purge is based on two small shrubs, one native in Egypt and the Sudan and usually called Alexandrian senna because it is shipped from that port.

The other and by far the more important is an Arabian shrub now little grown in that country. Long ago this small shrub was taken to extreme southern India and cultivated on such a scale near Tinnevelly that it is usually called Tinnevelly senna. Three quarters of the world's supply of senna now comes from these hot, steaming plantations which are not too far from a famous and beautifully sculptured Siva temple.

Both the shrubs belong to a large genus of plants called by the botanists *Cassia*. One of the four hundred species is perfectly familiar to the subtropical gardener as the golden shower (*Cassia Fistula*). It is a medium-sized tree from India, much cultivated in Florida, with showy hanging clusters of yellow, pea-like flowers and long pods.

But the cassias that yield senna are quite different. Alexandrian senna is a shrub (*Cassia acutifolia*) usually not over two and a half feet high, with a leaf composed of two to six stalkless leaflets (the Alexandrian senna of commerce) and small, pea-like yellow flowers. Except for small plantations in India, most Alexandrian senna is collected from wild plants in northern Africa.

Tinnevelly senna plantations in India now cover several thousand acres. The shrub (*Cassia angustifolia*) was originally raised from seed, taken from Arabia to southern India, and does not grow much over two and a half feet high. Its leaf has four to eight leaflets (the Tinnevelly senna of commerce) and yellow, small, pea-like flowers. The experts all agree that the medicinal value of senna is quite independent of whether the leaflets come from Alexandrian senna or are derived from what is called Indian senna, which, of course, comes from Tinnevelly.

Senna is a purge, and sometimes a little griping, but it is much milder than many of its more drastic relatives. Like a few other cathartics, it acts chiefly in evacuating the contents of the colon in six to eight hours after taking the drug. This

Senna: a mild cathartic, now grown in India

is used mostly as the dry powder of the leaflets after they have been cleaned and crushed. But it is also dispensed as a fluid extract of senna. Its use, except in drugstore nostrums, should be prescribed by a physician.

In England, but rarely in the United States, doctors prefer the powdered pods of senna as a little less griping than the leaves, but other British authorities scoff at this. The use of the pods by the ancient Arabians, however, was quite common. Both the leaves and the pods appear to contain emodin, which is also found in rhubarb, and is responsible, in part, for the cathartic action of these small leaflets.

A little confusion exists among the uninitiated as to the difference between the cassias that produce senna and cassia bark. The latter is the aromatic bark of an Indian tree known as *Cinnamomum Cassia,* a relative of cinnamon and so persistently fragrant and spicy that it was used to make the holy incense of the early Jews.

The Soothing Purge

Somewhere in tropical Africa or in India and centuries before recorded history, there grew a striking, large-leaved tree of medium size, with a terminal cluster of greenish flowers, followed by a smooth or prickly capsule containing beautifully marbled seeds. Hardly any seed in the world furnishes a better illustration of the vagaries of Nature than these deceptively innocent-looking and frankly attractive castor oil beans. But they are deadly poisonous, and the record of the fatalities caused by them is voluminous.

Besides the active poison, the seeds contain such a valuable, bland oil that consumption of it is almost beyond belief. The United States uses over three hundred million pounds annually of the seeds from which the oil is extracted, and imports many additional millions of pounds of the oil extracted elsewhere.

A seed that contains an active poison and also yields from 45-50 per cent of a bland oil presented problems to the early users of it. It is still a highly technical process to harvest the oil without also having it contaminated by the poison. Heating the seeds, which is a common extractive process of other oil seeds, merely distributes the poison into the oil.

Finally it was found that if the hulled seeds were crushed between rollers, at a temperature not over 50°, the oil would come out of the press without a trace of poison. This is the safe, bland, widely used and nauseating castor oil!

The lay public has nothing but curses for this important remedy, but it would be hard to find a cathartic more favored by the physician. Even Dr. Peter Canvane of Bath, in 1764, praised it because more "drastic rough purges are condemned by all with great justice as they draw the intestines into spasmodic contractions, and add irritation to irritation."

A century and a half later the distinguished Dr. Bernard

Fantus, who called castor oil "The Soothing Purge," did so because of its great therapeutic qualities, and in spite of "its notoriously nasty taste." That taste is today usually masked by fruit juices. In most modern preparations the nauseating taste is removed, which some think reduces the effectiveness of the remedy.

Unlike many cathartics, castor oil does not confine its activity to the colon, but begins almost at once to irritate rather mildly the whole intestinal tract. Within three or four hours, sometimes sooner, it will completely evacuate the material and relieve what Dr. Canvane called with brutal frankness "the dry bellyache."

Because the Romans thought the beautifully marbled seeds looked like a tick, they named the plant *Ricinus,* which is the Latin name for that insect. And *Ricinus communis* it has been ever since. It is cultivated throughout the world in warm regions, and there are many thousands of acres of a dwarf variety of it grown in the southwestern United States and in California, mostly for industrial uses.

All these oil-yielding plants are cultivated as annuals, as the original tree-like forms so common in the tropics are too difficult to harvest. Most temperate zone gardeners know it as a striking, summer-bedding annual, sometimes with handsome colored leaves, but usually these are deep green, long-stalked and from twenty to thirty-six inches wide. The castor oil plant, as grown for ornament, may be four to eight feet high but is much lower as harvested for industry. Perhaps the only direction for the amateur growers is to warn all children about the poison in the attractively colored seeds. One or two of them, within a few hours, are almost sure to be fatal.

The Egyptians and the Romans knew castor oil very well. Some of its seeds have even been rescued from ancient tombs thousands of years old, and Pliny wrote of it in the first century, "Castor oil, taken with an equal quantity of water, acts as a purgative upon the bowels." In spite of such distinguished sponsorship, it lapsed as a remedy, partly, no doubt, because of its repulsive taste, but also because careless extraction of the oil might poison the patient.

Not until 1788 was it admitted into the London *Pharmacopœia,* largely due to Dr. Canvane of Bath. This observant physician had practiced in the West Indies, where the Spanish name for the plant was Palma Christi. There he studied it, convinced of its mild efficacy as a purge. But he also found that the natives of the British and French islands had other uses for castor oil. They were employing it for "temperating all febrile heats, especially the heats of venery."

Little of the enormous importation and United States production of castor oil is ever used as medicine. The chief uses of the oil, and of the residue of the seeds left after the extraction of the oil, are in the manufacture of soap, plastics, tiles and as a superior lubricating oil. Curiously enough, one of its derivatives is an ingredient of perfumes!

The Holy Bark

Sedentary city folk have no monopoly on constipation. It afflicts soldiers, explorers and travelers just as frequently as those glued to the drudgery of desk work. It is these unfortunates who run to the drugstore for nostrums, many of them containing one or more of the ingredients already discussed. Goodman and Gilman in their scholarly *Pharmacological Basis of Therapeutics* merely reflect the opinion of thoughtful doctors when they write that while cathartics are more used than almost any other medicine, "there is a needlessly large number of such drugs."

The public, for thousands of years, has been deaf to such pronouncements. So were those early Spanish missionaries who pushed up from Mexico in the eighteenth century, first saw the incomparable redwood trees and founded San Francisco. Later one of them, whose name evades historical records, went north to the Oregon border and found what many think is the most widely used cathartic on earth.

This padre found the Indians of northern California and Oregon using as a cathartic the bark of a medium-sized tree or large shrub. So efficacious and mild was it that it was promptly christened cascara sagrada—the sacred or holy bark. It is now for sale in practically every drugstore on earth. It has never been synthesized and is not much cultivated, so that Portland is still the market place to which the bark strippers bring their annual harvest from wild trees.

Several relatives of cascara sagrada grow in California and Oregon, and some of them creep eastward to Idaho and Montana. The medicinal one, known as *Rhamnus purshiana,* was so named in honor of F. T. Pursh, a German botanical explorer who, however, never visited California. It is most common in northern California and Oregon but stretches up through Washington to southern British Columbia.

For such an important tree, cascara sagrada is a singularly drab and even undistinguished plant. Its thin leaves and inconspicuous greenish flowers, followed by blackish, berry-like fruits, appear to be a striking contrast to the value of its rather thin grayish-brown bark. The collection of this may be four or five million pounds a year.

Such figures give one no idea of the almost complete eclipse of cascara for over a hundred years after its discovery. Not until 1877 did eastern drug manufacturers know much about it, but in that year samples of the bark were sent to Detroit for investigation by a pharmaceutical firm. Today a large botanical drug company in New York maintains a branch in Portland to buy the bark. This is very thin, intensely bitter, and that bitterness is an insurance against substitution of inferior bark. Chewing true fresh cascara sagrada practically kills all sense of taste for hours. Ultimately, in the finished drug, the taste is masked, or the finely ground bark is put into the familar chocolate-coated pill and there is no bitterness unless one is naïve enough to crush it.

Bark collecting is so simple that itinerant laborers do a good deal of it. The bark slips easily from the trunk, which is finally stripped of it and the tree cut down. From the stump new growth will start, so that in spite of the huge annual harvest the tree is far from extinction. In drying, it loses about half its weight; the harvest of fresh bark is thus practically twice as great as the finished product.

The huge popularity of cascara sagrada has a sound basis. Its active constituents do not differ enough from those found in rhubarb and senna to be technically significant. But the alchemy of Nature has made it less objectionable than most other purges, because, as one expert puts it, "the action is mild and unaccompanied by discomfort or griping." But its effectiveness is practically certain, as it causes a complete evacuation of the bowels in about eight hours. Overdosing, as in any other drug, can cause complications, and no doctor advocates its indiscriminate or continued use. Again, the public seems to be skeptical, judging by its enormous lay consumption.

The only real objection to cascara sagrada is its intense bitterness. When it was first introduced, about 1878, this kept many from taking it. Doctors were warned that "it should not be prescribed in its bitter form without asking the patient whether he is willing to take bitter medicine." Many declined, but the problem was finally solved by putting it in pleasant-tasting sugar-coated or chocolate-coated pills. These are admittedly less effective than the fluid extract of the bark, but the pills compensate for this by containing an increased quantity of the powdered bark.

While cascara is thus almost the only American cathartic,

Dioscorides in his *De Materia Medica,* written in the first century of our era, suspected a relative of it might have cathartic properties. This was the Avignon-berry (*Rhamnus infectoria*) of southern Europe. That prince of ancient doctors wrote that it was good "for such as are troubled with ye colic and disenterie." It is now obsolete and the American bark reigns supreme.

There are at least two other plant cathartics more violent and drastic than any of the above. They are little used, even by the doctors, and one hopes never by the lay public. Physicians use them only when immediate evacuation is imperative, as, for instance, in some cases of food poisoning. They may be even life-saving in such an emergency, but they are intensely irritating and so work within two or three hours.

One of them is Colocynth, derived from the fruit of a plant called the bitter apple (*Citrullus colocynthis*), which grows in India. It is a scrambling vine with solitary yellow flowers, followed by a roundish smooth fruit about three inches in diameter. Related to it is a small, straggling vine, prostrate on the ground in southern Europe. It also has yellow flowers, but its oblong fruit is prickly. Doctors know it as Elaterin, but the botanists call it *Ecballium elaterium,* the famous squirting cucumber.

The juice of the fruit of both these plants provides about the most drastic and violent of the purges. Both of them are not very distant cousins of the common cucumber, which may suggest to some why they think that vegetable just misses being a poison.

If, as so many physicians deplore, Nature has been a bit too lavish with her plant cathartics, the public, apparently, couldn't care less. The huge lay consumption of them, plus the sodium, potassium and magnesium substitutes, is staggering. Then, too, there are the so-called "bulk cathartics" like psyllium, agar and bran, most of which have the merely mechanical property of increasing the bulk of the contents of the alimentary tract rather than the definite medical action of true cathartics.

If the public believed the doctors instead of running to the drugstore, they would heed one of the most distinguished of them. He wrote:

"We must not permit the patient to make of his bowel a fetish for daily and devoted worship."

African arrow poison that became ouabain

11. The Helpful Poisoners

THE ART OF POISONING has suffered a drastic decline. Greek and Roman practitioners were so adept that patrician families hired them to obliterate an undesirable, and often had a taster in the household for their own protection. The art was so well known in Rome that it occasioned only mild surprise when twenty Roman ladies of the highest standing, under the direction of Cornelia and Sergia, poisoned "their husbands or others who had become inconvenient to them." Rather than stand the ordeal of their trial, they drank their own fatal brew.

From the earliest eras, poisoning became a profession, usually with the connivance of the local pharmacy. It was so skillful that the practitioners guaranteed the victims would be eliminated in three days, six months or a year, whichever suited the convenience of those who hired them. Because of their delayed action, it was usually impossible to ascribe the death to any particular plant, but least of all to arsenic, which was a famous eliminator of the unwanted.

In the Middle Ages the art flourished, especially under the Borgia and Medici families. Even King John of England was charged with having Maud Fitzwalter poisoned in the Tower because she refused to become his mistress. Crime and intrigue, plus the "legal" poisoning by the Venetian Council of Ten, seem to have dulled the public into acquiescence of death by the diabolical arts, then mostly hatched in a pharmacy.

Today poisoning has become rather rare, perhaps because our detection of the poison and the poisoner is so much better than in the days of the Borgias, when exposure was next to impossible. We read in detective fiction of a few cases where Agatha Christie, Ngaio Marsh or Rex Stout each has a victim die suddenly and horribly from prussic acid. This derivative of the kernels of the bitter almond kills so quickly that it is often a matter of seconds rather than minutes or hours between ingestion and death. The crudity and speed of it would have digusted the talented Medicis, whose methods were insidious and the effects often long-delayed.

Such drugs came and must come from a pharmacy, which is now difficult, as most governments restrict their sale. But pharmacies, from the Greek and Roman days, have been so identified with poisoning that the orignal Greek word *pharmakeia* was usually associated not only with medicines but with poisons, especially with the tipping of arrows with some lethal brew. These poisoned-tipped arrows had a Greek name from which the Latin *toxicum* is derived—now shortened to our English *toxic*.

Poisoned arrows are as old as history. Virgil in the *Aeneid* has one of his characters described as:

There was no other man more skilled of hand than his
In tincturing darts and arming steel with poison.

Five centuries before Virgil, Homer has Odysseus
Seeking the deadly drug, wherewith to anoint his bronze-tipped
arrows.

And even the Bible records these deadly darts when Job
laments that "the poison whereof drinketh up my spirit." As
late as the days of Marco Polo (1254-1324), that intrepid
traveler cited a section of China where "all their arrows were
poisoned."

The use of poisoned arrows for warfare or the chase is perhaps preferable to the insidious brews of the professional
poisoners hired to eliminate the unwanted. War and the
chase were after all normal, masculine exhibitions of prowess.
The pitting of one's knowledge of poison-tipped arrows
against men or animals always carried the hazard that you
might yourself be a victim.

All over the world primitive people have used them and
this practice exists today in parts of South America and Africa.
In the latter strife-torn continent, as late as 1964, an American
missionary was killed by a poisoned arrow shot into her back.
Some of these poisons kill quickly, but others take enough
time so that a patient may be saved if a physician and the
antidote are handy. This, of course, rarely happens, and, until
recently, the composition of the poison was often a tribal
secret.

In the January, 1964, issue of *Atlas,* there is an article by
Bethwell Ogot, reprinted from *Transition,* a monthly review
published in Uganda. He cites the difficulty in making his
own people understand democracy, for they have always lived
under a tribal chief, chosen because he embodied their
ancient mores. But if the chief departed from traditional customs, he was asked to "open the calabash—that is, to commit

suicide." The calabash was merely a kind of gourd containing the lethal dose.

These poisons became, rather recently, the objects of massive research. What juice or bark or seed, or what combination of them, killed so effectively? And why did some of these poisons leave the killed animal with flesh that was perfectly safe as food? Did such poisons affect only the nervous system and the brain? If so, how did some of the most primitive people in the world discover the highly selective action of the poisons? And, finally, could some of these lethal doses contain an active constituent that might be a valuable drug?

Such questions sparked a search of often lurid literature and sent many explorers to remote jungles in Venezuela, Surinam, Peru, Ecuador, Colombia, tropical Africa, Madagascar and Java. Most of these botanical hunters of drug plants knew of Sir Walter Raleigh's vivid description of one of them when he wrote, in 1595:

There was nothing whereof I was more curious than to find out the true remedies of these poisoned arrows. For besides the mortality of the wounds they make, the party shot endureth the most insufferable torment in the world and abideth a most ugly and lamentable death.

A few such whispers from the earth also set the drug specialists, especially the pharmacologists, to ask the final question. Are any of these poisons of use in medicine? Surely some of them might be used in diseases of the nervous system, perhaps even of the brain.

Behind such queries there was a fantastic plethora of lurid and often untrue legends. It was even stated by an explorer that one of the African tribes that used these arrows was convinced that great valor came only by eating the testicles of the enemy. Other travelers brought home bizarre tales of black magic, wholesale poisoning, and even the well-nigh incredible stories of the ordeal poisoners, which ultimately turned out to be true in parts of tropical Africa and Madagascar.

But scientists ultimately answered most of these questions. They definitely proved that the leaf, bark, root, juice or seed of the plants used to prepare these lethal potions contained active constituents which have become drugs of incalculable value. Such discoveries made it clear enough that no matter how primitive their originators, the natives have in fact become extremely helpful poisoners. Their stories and what came of them leads us first to Java, through Madagascar to tropical Africa, and finally to the New World.

The Tree That Fooled Erasmus Darwin

In 1789, the famous grandfather of Charles Darwin wrote a longish poem called the *Loves of the Plants,* later incorporated into his much longer *The Botanic Garden* (1803). A somewhat bombastic nature and a far from critical mind led him to repeat one of the most fantastic botanical canards ever to amaze the British public.

It originated in Java, once governed by the British, but generally considered as the most important island of the former Netherlands East Indies. Here grows a gigantic tree, with a milky juice and a history about as reliable as the current spate of so-called "science fiction." The juice is violently poisonous and has been used for centuries by the natives to smear the tips of their arrows and often for less legitimate ends.

The tree is the notorious Upas, the latter a Javanese name for any poison. Actually the native names for it vary from anchar, antsjar and hypo to ipoh, which it is generally called in Malaya. As to the violent nature of its poison, there is no question, for it is deadly. Such lethal qualities in a handsome tree were sure to spark inquiry and much loose speculation.

It seems as if its unquestionably poisonous sap was not enough for the incredulous early travelers. They repeated native superstition and magic tales and invented some marvels of their own. It was not long before these European chroniclers ascribed an horrendous quality to the Upas tree that is palpably absurd.

Many trees, due to their own shade or the drip from their leaves, have little or nothing growing under them, and the Upas is no exception. Upon this perfectly normal ecological reaction there grew up and was broadcast to the world the "fact" that the tree exhaled a poisonous "gas" which killed all vegetation near it and "destroys all animal life within a radius of fifteen miles!" It was this nonsense that Erasmus Darwin used in his *The Botanic Garden* and that is still swallowed by incredulous readers of the more lurid Sunday supplements.

To explode it, an Englishman subsequently visited Java, climbed up the tree, had lunch there, smoked a cigar and was aloft for about two hours. Absolutely nothing happened. But long before this and even before the Dutch made their first settlement in Java, the tree had a fantastic history. Java for many years was still under the partial control of petty "kings," who governed different sections of an island as large as Cuba. They hated the Dutch and sometimes poisoned their wells with Upas juice.

Some of these local potentates lived in rather opulent splendor, complete with palaces, jewels, concubines and other evidences of wealth and power. In 1776 an unfortunate interruption came to this idyllic scene when thirteen concubines of one of these kings "were convicted of infidelity to the emperor's bed."

The thirteen girls were each fastened to a post and their breasts bared. The executioner, with an awl-like instrument, poisoned with the gum of the Upas, lanced the unhappy wretches in the middle of their breasts. All of them died within five minutes in the greatest agonies.

The latex of the Upas is certainly one of the most deadly of all the plant poisons and has been used in the past for getting rid of undesirable natives of Java, often including the Dutch, whose armies of conquest were sadly depleted by arrows tipped with Upas. Men pierced by such arrows died rather quickly "in violent tetanus convulsions."

The Upas, ultimately christened *Antiaris toxicaria*, is a member of the mulberry family (Moraceae) and grows not only in Java but in Borneo, Burma, India and Ceylon. It is a huge tree, sometimes as high as two hundred fifty feet, with the first branches from sixty to eighty feet above the ground. Its milky juice coagulates in the air and is tapped much like the rubber trees to which it is not related. The inner bark is fibrous, felty and can be removed easily; especially is this true in India, where the plant is known as the sacking tree. Small branches are made into legs of trousers and arms of coats, the larger ones forming the backs of the garments. So safe is this cleansed inner bark that sacks made of it are extensively used for storing rice.

This innocent use of the Upas is emphatically not matched by the constituents of its latex, which is bitter and biting to those who dare taste even a drop of it. When dried, the latex becomes of the consistency of a "thick dark-brown resinous gum." This is reputed to be quite harmless if taken by mouth, for the Upas does its deadly work only if it enters the blood stream.

This fact was well known to the natives who were tipping their arrows with it for centuries. They designed these lethal weapons with an easily detachable, very sharp point. This would stay in the wound, even if the arrow was pulled out immediately, so that death followed within a few moments.

They also found that an ordinary arrow tip, smeared with Upas, would make such a big puncture that the rush of blood might dilute the poison and defeat their intent to kill.

Such a drastic poison could not escape the scrutiny of the pharmacologist, and finally a constituent was isolated from Upas gum and called *antiarin*. It is a violent poison to the heart, but in proper dilution its effects are sufficiently valuable so that Dr. W. Straub of Leipzig published an account of it in 1929. From 1910 Dr. Straub had been studying drugs that might have the same effect on the heart as digitalis. Among these were several African arrow poisons, and he found that, with proper care, antiarin might be a substitute for digitalis. Some Russian scientists, who repeated the canard that fooled Erasmus Darwin, also thought that antiarin might be useful. Still later, in 1948, three Swiss scientists were contrasting the toxicity of antiarin with other heart remedies.

Today antiarin is in no pharmacopoeia and hence has no official standing in medical practice. It is included here mostly for its having sparked research upon a plant long discredited as a fabulous East Indian killer. In the worldwide hunt for heart remedies, the plant hunters could not ignore the Upas, for so violent a poison, even if it did not produce a valuable drug, might point the way to organic chemists in their equally urgent hunt for synthetics.

Ordeal by Tanghin

About 3,500 miles across the Indian Ocean in a southwesterly direction from Java lies one of the largest islands in the world, now called the Republic of Madagascar. Originally Portuguese, then French, it comprises a mixture of people, partly Negroes from Africa, some Arabians and several races originally from India and countries further east.

Not too far from the African coast, near Mozambique, the

island is practically all tropical, and its vegetation contains many plants found nowhere else. One of the most striking is the enormous traveler's-tree with a huge cluster of banana-like leaves at the end of a tall trunk. It contains so much pure, potable water that its use suggested the name to thirsty travelers.

Another endemic, and by far the most notorious, tree is known as the tanghin, the effects of which were so drastic that the French put a stop to its use years ago. It is about the size of an apple tree, and bears evergreen leaves and a showy terminal cluster of pinkish flowers, the tube of which is greenish. These are followed by a purplish-tinged fruit somewhat like a small apple, containing a rather woody nut or seed, which Swinburne called the "sullen savour of poisonous pain."

The tree belongs to the dogbane family (Apocynaceae), which contains many poisonous plants, most of which have a milky juice. It was originally and appropriately named *Tanghinia venenifera*, the latter meaning poison-bearing. Such are the vagaries of botanical nomenclature that the plant is now called, by the pedantic, *Cerbera tanghin*, which tells us nothing of its diabolical uses.

Long before the French took over in 1883, there were a series of kings and queens in Madagascar who ruled most of the island with somewhat despotic powers. This was the so-called Hova regime, which, if they did not invent the ordeal by tanghin, enormously increased its scope.

It was well known by the natives that the tanghin seeds were violently poisonous and could be used to eliminate enemies, but the ordeal nature of its use came with the relatively settled government under the Hovas. With courts of a kind and at least the semblance of a trial for the accused, Madagascar had what looked like a primitive jurisprudence.

The trials were simplicity itself. The accused, whether a

murderer, a thief, or merely a neighbor quarreling about land or a debt, was forced to drink a brew of tanghin. If he was knowing, he swallowed it at a gulp and promptly vomited. Such a person was accredited as "innocent." If he was stupid and afraid, he sipped the brew slowly and would be dead almost immediately and, of course, "guilty."

With the judge, or his masters, having complete control of the strength of the potion, it is easy to predict what happened to Madagascar and why it became necessary for the French to stop the scandalous ordeal poisoning of the regime. The Hovas had many petty insurrections and literally thousands of natives, accused of "treason," were forced to drink the most infamous ordeal poison in the world.

If they refused to drink it, they were killed at once by a soldier's spear, or sometimes offered an alternative. This was to swim a crocodile-infested river; if they landed safely, they were said to be innocent.

These amenities of Madagascan justice became notorious in the European press; and just before the turn of the century English, French and German anthropologists and other scientists went to what was largely an unknown island. Some of them could scarcely find a tanghin tree, for the good reason that the French governor had ordered their destruction. But in remote spots of the interior, where French rule was rather sketchy, the ordeal by tanghin was still practiced.

It soon became evident that the poison was found only in the seed or nut, and speculation became rife as to its active constituents. In weak doses it acted merely as an emetic, but the ordeal brews were deadly. Seeds were taken to London, and from them were isolated two active principles called *tanghinin* and *cerberin*.

Their isolation did not make much of an impression on the great pharmacological laboratories of the world, for they were busy testing the properties of dozens of other plants. Much of their research was aimed at producing heart remedies better than digitalis. Finally in a laboratory in Russia *tanghinin* was tried on some experimental animals. Those that died from too large a dose were autopsied, and it appeared that poisonous concentrations affected the heart. But in less concentrated form the drug reduced the rapidity of the heart rate and strengthened it—not unlike the action of digitalis.

But tanghinin never did replace digitalis. It is in no modern pharmacopoeia and can be ignored except by that devoted band of scientists who are always listening to such whispers from the earth on the chance that a healing drug may lurk in the shadows. They well knew that tanghin belongs to the dogbane family and that years ago David Livingstone sent from tropical Africa the seed of a plant in that family which ultimately became world-famous.

David Livingstone's Contribution

For many years, starting in 1849, this devout missionary and traveler was so intrepid and spectacularly successful in his exploration of tropical Africa that the British, on his death in 1873, buried him in Westminster Abbey. Two years before, ill, half-starved and nearly dead, he was rescued from a remote section of tropical Africa by Henry M. Stanley, who greeted him with the well-publicized "Dr. Livingstone, I presume!" This was on November 10, 1871, long after Livingstone's contribution to the geography, ethnology and botany of the Dark Continent had aroused the enthusiasm and respect of all the world.

In 1861, on one of his expeditions, starting from Capetown, he reached the Shiré River, near Mozambique, where he found the tribes using poisoned arrows. He wrote to London, "The poison used here, called Kombi, is obtained from a species of *Strophanthus*." For a brief statement it raised a remarkable scientific furor, for that plant belonged to the dogbane family (Apocynaceae), and every botanist and pharmacologist knew the violently poisonous nature of many plants in that family, such as the tanghin in the neighboring island of Madagascar, and in our common oleander.

The tribesmen found by Livingstone were using arrows twenty-nine to thirty-seven inches long, shot from a bow, and tipped with a poison derived from the seeds of what was ultimately called *Strophanthus kombé*. *Strophanthus kombé*, as a name, has been since replaced by *Strophanthus hispidus*, which was once thought to apply to a closely related species. Today *S. hispidus* is the accepted name. It was soon found that there were many other species of *Strophanthus* scattered all over tropical Africa, much to the confusion of later explorers, especially those who sought from one of them a source of Cortisone as late as 1949. The genus *Strophanthus* was first discovered in Java in 1795. Some species grow in India, but the greatest concentration of them is in tropical Africa.

Not until Livingstone's report was it suspected that *Strophanthus hispidus* was anything more than a scrambling vine with pale, cream-colored, slightly twisted flowers having a tail-like prolongation of the corolla that might be eight to ten inches long. These are followed by a pair of long, slender pods twelve to fifteen inches long, with many small seeds. The natives pound these to a pulp and coagulate the mass to a consistency, making it possible to smear the arrow tips for five or six inches. An animal shot with such an arrow is "rarely able to move a hundred yards, and the flesh is eaten without bad effect."

The plant was ultimately found to grow as far north as Lake Tanganyika, but apparently not in central or west Africa. Seeds of it, after much experimental work, finally yielded an active constituent called *strophanthin,* which has a digitalis-like action on the heart, but with a difference that is vital. As it is derived from such a poisonous plant, physicians are warned, *"Strophanthin is extremely poisonous."* It cannot be given by mouth, as is so often done with digitalis, but must be injected into a vein in doses as small as 1/100 of a grain. And if the patient has had any digitalis within the last week or so, strophanthin "may cause sudden death."

Why use such a potentially dangerous drug? It is life-saving in cardiac emergencies, for it acts much faster than digitalis, the beneficial effects of which may not begin for several hours. Hence strophanthin is used in critical emergencies involving the heart, acute edema of the lungs, and in several other contingencies. While its action is rapid, it is also transient, so that it is often followed with slower-acting medication.

How could anyone expect that such a savage tribe would also be helpful poisoners? But they found a substance that would produce a life-saving drug. Like so many of the tribes of Africa, they were extremely primitive. So much so, that as late as 1920 a couple of British explorers reported that if "a girl baby cuts the first two upper incisors before the lower teeth make their appearance, the child is usually strangled and thrown into a stagnant pool."

Least of all did anyone suspect that this faint whisper from the earth would lead to the finding of other plants of the dogbane family yielding an even more valuable drug than strophanthin.

The Story of Ouabain

The *United States Pharmacopœia* admits this African drug into the select category of standard remedies, a distinction not shared by the closely related strophanthin. Ouabain, the mod-

ern version of the African *wabayo* or *ouabaio,* is also derived
from another species of *Strophanthus* and from a tree called
Acokanthera, both belonging to the dogbane family.

Among better-known plants in this family are the native
Indian hemp (*Apocynum cannabinum*) and, among garden
plants, the periwinkle (*Vinca minor*), the oleander (*Nerium
Oleander*) and the gorgeous *Allamanda.* But none of these
furnishes a deadly arrow poison like ouabain, and while almost any plant in that family is legitimately suspect, their
effects cannot compare with these primitive messengers of
death.

The chief source of ouabain is *Strophanthus gratus,* a shrub
or small tree quite unlike its scrambling relative that yields
strophanthin. Livingstone found that the natives called the
latter kombi. Ouabain is confined to tropical Africa among a
people so primitive that one exploring expedition reported
that:

Pregnant women are believed to be dangerous to newborn children, to calabashes in a garden, to fruit on a tree, to a litter of
puppies and to the eggs on which a hen is setting.

But primitive or not, these people found, and have known
for centuries, that the seeds of ouabain, properly mashed and
coagulated, yielded an arrow poison so deadly that few animals, including man, survive more than a few moments. And
for such a giant as an elephant, they tipped a spear which,
driven into the hide of the monster, would stop its lumbering
gait.

Another and official source of ouabain is quite different
from *Strophanthus gratus.* It comes from one or two species of
trees in Abyssinia and eastern Africa, and the poison is derived from the wood. The best known of these are *Acokanthera schimperi* and *A. deflexa,* both medium-sized trees.
From the pulverized wood of these and perhaps other species

of *Acokanthera* comes a decidedly secondary source of ouabain.

Hunting and fighting with this poison have been going on for centuries. And there is one feature of its use that neither the botanist nor pharmacologist can explain, although it excites the admiration of both. The very concept of a plant family is a sophisticated discipline that many educated people find rather baffling. And yet these African primitives who knew nothing about the dogbane family (Apocynaceae) chose the seeds of one and the wood of another, not only to poison their arrows but unintentionally to supply us with an extremely valuable heart remedy.

Few whispers from the earth have been more useful than ouabain. It is today a widely used drug for some types of heart disease, and its speed of action is so great that it is frequently life-saving. Three or five minutes after injection the heart responds—far faster than with the old, reliable digitalis. It is preferred by many cardiologists to the closely related strophanthin.

Some of the people who produce it live among the huge phallic monuments in southern Abyssinia. Others inhabit mud huts in east Africa. But modern medical experts have listened so well to these primitive tribesmen that they forget or may not know how much their magic and superstition may have contributed to final victory.

At one place where ouabain and strophanthin are used by the natives, Dr. T. R. Fraser of Edinburgh, who worked for years on the constituents of these plants, wrote that:

No evidence can be found of *Strophanthus* being used by the natives as a medicinal substance. They have a great dread of it in the treatment of disease, and thought the people in England using it as a medicine must be mad to employ so poisonous a substance.

They were quite right to fear ouabain as a medicine. It is still so dangerous that physicians prescribing it usually limit the dose to 1/120 of a grain or even less. And like strophanthin, giving it to a patient who has taken any digitalis within the last week or ten days is apt to be fatal. Such refinements of medication seem a bit remote from those helpful poisoners who started it all. They still live in Africa, and even as late as 1920 Smith and Dale reported:

A chief's wives, children and slaves used to be "buried" with him. If any stranger happened to pass, he was promptly killed and added to the pile.

This was a funeral fire.

Blindness, Tired Muscles, and a Big Belly

For centuries untreated glaucoma blinded untold multitudes of people, especially in the tropics. Its cause is still unknown, but its cure or at least its control is now within the competence of any good eye doctor. It may start insidiously with only a slight impairment of vision, and is often confined to those in the later years of life. At first the most noticeable symptom is seeing double or the apparent halo around a bright light. Gradually, and without treatment, the vision gets progressively dimmer until there is complete loss of sight, which is never regained. Long before the dread finale of this disease, there is an agonizing pain in the eyeball due to what ophthalmologists call ocular tension. This leads to severe headaches, followed often by nausea and vomiting, a combination of symptoms sufficiently dreadful to frighten any patient, not to speak of the gradual loss of vision. No remedy was known until after Dr. Daniell, a British missionary in west Africa, sent to London in 1840 some seeds of a plant the natives called esere.

From that same plant, and its modern derivatives, came a spectacular remedy for another disease of unknown cause more likely to affect women than men. It begins at first with that tired feeling, especially toward evening, when the accumulated stresses of the day are reflected in weakness of the muscles. Often women between twenty and fifty years of age, who are most likely to get it, think it is nothing but normal tiredness. But they may be completely wrong, for things are happening to their nerve impulses and hence to the muscles that are "fed" by such impulses that only a doctor can appraise. He well knows that myasthenia gravis, which is the technical name of the disease, can produce an alarming progression to double vision, and that the muscles of the neck, throat, lips, tongue and face become infected, but not usually those of the trunk or legs. The trouble may persist for years, or it may be quickly fatal, due to respiratory failure.

Still another and less alarming trouble owes its amelioration to Dr. Daniell's studies among the tribesmen in west Africa. Often after an abdominal operation the surgeon is worried, and so is the patient, by an alarmingly distended abdomen. If not corrected, it can lead to distressing and even dangerous sequelae. The distension is caused by an accumulation of gas, and scarcely anything is so effective as a hypodermic injection of one of the derivatives of the seed of the plant found in Calabar by the perceptive Dr. Daniell.

He spent some years in the southeastern corner of Nigeria and in the neighboring regions of west Africa and in 1840 found the seeds of a plant which he sent to London. These came from Calabar, a native seaport on the edge of a region of vast mangrove swamps, some of them eighty miles wide, and through which flowed sluggish rivers. In the upland part of the area lived many different tribes, and from one of them he secured what have ever since been called Calabar beans, which are violently poisonous. The natives called them esere.

Dr. Daniell was no doubt familiar enough with the use of these beans, for they were "the state ordeal poison" of the natives. Years later, in 1863, Dr. T. R. Fraser wrote a medical paper entitled, "The characters, actions and therapeutic uses of the Ordeal Bean of Calabar." He pointed out that "the mode of trial by ordeal is extremely ancient," citing from Chapter 5 of the book of Numbers, where it was used to detect a case of "conjugal unfaithfulness."

It was used in Calabar exactly as was the tanghin in Madagascar, where the medicine man, acting for the chief, would brew the poison according to determine whether the prisoner was destined to be found "guilty" because he died, or "innocent" if the poison was weak or he immediately vomited and he therefore lived.

It is difficult to trace the transition from these jungle ethics to the final appraisal of the Calabar beans in British laboratories. First of all had to come the identification of the plant that produced the beans. They grow on a large woody vine, often fifty to sixty feet high and with a stem two to three inches thick, having a compound leaf consisting of only three leaflets. The beautiful, pea-like, pinkish flowers are borne in showy drooping clusters, followed by a pea-like pod six to seven inches long, each containing only two or three kidney-shaped seeds.

These are about one and a half inches long, brown or blackish, and are the notorious and deadly Calabar beans. No other part of the plant is poisonous. It was subsequently named *Physostigma venenosum;* it is a member of the pea family and not so distantly related to wisteria. From its seeds was isolated the alkaloid *physostigmine* which opened up the varied and useful medical attributes of the Calabar bean.

It took physicians quite a few years to learn the values and dangers of physostigmine, but it finally became clear that it had a variety of uses besides its effectiveness in glaucoma, myasthenia gravis and its reduction of gas in a post-operative abdomen. From a study of its chemical structure was evolved neostigmine (prostigmine), a purely synthetic drug which is preferred by many doctors, especially in glaucoma and myasthenia gravis. By a carefully designed program of neostigmine a patient with the latter disease may be rescued from a state of having little muscle power, and hence being practically helpless, to becoming almost normal. But continuous use of either drug may build up an immunity to them, and death from the disease may follow, unless other therapy is instituted.

Several other uses of physostigmine and its analogue neostigmine have been adopted into modern practice. They tend, for instance, to slow the pulse and by dilating the arteries reduce blood pressure. And besides reducing abdominal flatulence after operations, the drugs have a beneficial effect on the muscles of the intestines and hence help a somewhat inert evacuation to become more active. They also reduce the heartburn that may accompany pregnancy.

And besides their beneficial effect in glaucoma, they contract the pupil where ophthalmologists need such effects, promote sweating and have several other minor uses. Of course these derivatives of the Calabar bean are themselves dangerously poisonous and hence given with extreme care.

Their final and quite valuable quality is to act as an antidote for overdoses of another drug that acts as a muscle relaxant. The horrible effects of the ordeal poison of Calabar were due to the paralysis of the muscles that control respiration, so that the victims died of asphyxiation. Centuries before this, some South American Indians had discovered in the jungle another poison known to every surgeon, for it, too, relaxes muscles. Overdoses of this can be quickly fatal, but an antidote for it, appropriately enough, is the derivative of the Calabar bean. Thus one poison provides an antidote for another—the last of the Helpful Poisoners, and this one from the New World.

The Story of Curare

For such a helpful poison, curare has a somewhat elusive history. It was first noticed by that brilliant young Spanish soldier, Pedro de Cieza de Leon about 1540, and noted in his *Chronica del Peru,* which was published at Seville in 1553. He found the Indians in the lowlands of Peru, Ecuador, Colombia and Brazil shooting arrows tipped with what was called "woorali," "urari," "curari," "wourari"—all of them native names for what we call curare, which is a deadly arrow poison.

In 1541 Francisco de Orellana, who named and was the first explorer to traverse the whole length of the mighty Amazon, lost one of his companions by an Indian shooting him with a curare-tipped arrow. He wrote, "The arrow did not penetrate half a finger, but, as it had poison on it, he gave up his soul to our Lord." And Sir Walter Raleigh in 1895 noted it in the Guianas, many miles eastward from Peru. He said the Indians "are very violent, or rather desperate people, and have the most strong poison on their arrows."

This proved, even before 1600, that curare was known from the Atlantic to the Amazonian face of the Andes, a distance of over 2,500 miles, most of it heavy rain-forest jungle. A few early explorers such as the French La Condamine, in 1745; the German Schomburgk (1836-47); and Martius (1830) wrote about it, as did the greatest of British plant explorers, Richard Spruce, whose *Notes of a Botanist on the Amazon and Andes* ultimately became a classic of exploration.

But as to what curare really was, what plants entered into its composition, and what it did to its victims, there was only the faintest notion. That ignorance lasted for the better part of two hundred years. Some of the Indians were hostile, and even the half-civilized were secretive about the ingredients and how they were prepared. Wherever such ignorance flourishes, rumor and cupidity quickly take over, and curare soon became a lurid morsel for sensational writers. Titles like "Flying Death," "Black Magic" and a dozen others caught the attention of the public far more than the quiet announcement in 1807 of Baron von Humboldt. He had actually discovered some of the ingredients and the lethal attributes of curare while on his expedition to the Amazon.

In 1811-12 Sir Benjamine Brodie, a distinguished British surgeon, took enough time off from his opposition to homeopathy to study the possibility that curare might, in spite of its undoubted dangers, become of medicinal value. Its active constituents were then unknown, but reports from the jungle were specific enough to convince him that animals shot with curare-tipped arrows died of asphyxiation. He tried artificial respiration on his experimental animals, and found it, at least in part, to be an antidote for the poison.

Still the active ingredient eluded investigation until Boussingault, a French agricultural chemist, and Roulin in 1828 isolated a syrupy substance which they called *curarin*. This was a discovery that did not help as much as curare historians hoped, for curare was not just curare, but was made by over twenty different tribes of South American Indians, and, according to lurid but not verifiable rumor, of as many ingredients. While it was known that most of the curares were made from different plants, the more sensational papers added snake venoms, boiled ants and anything else that would amaze the European public. Not unnaturally, curare became a front-page wonder rather than the therapeutic drug it was ultimately to be.

It was still obvious, however, that not enough was known about curare, and many scientific expeditions were sent to the jungle to clear up a whole mass of uncertainties. The Indians in different parts of South America were making three confusing types of the poison and named them according to the kind of containers they used for storing them. Hence came the terms "pot" curare, from its being in earthenware pots; "tube" curare, found in hollow bamboo tubes; and "gourd" or "calabash" curare, which was kept in the shell of the fruit of a gourd or calabash.

Such terminology was more diagnostic to the Indians than to the scientists, for it told them nothing as to the ingredients and least of all how curare was made. But by 1844 a brilliant French physiologist, Claude Bernard, evidently decided not to wait for final elucidation of the curare problem. He was so distinguished in his studies on the sympathetic nervous system that the Academie des Sciences awarded him three separate times its grand prize in physiology.

Bernard made an epoch-making discovery about curare. He, like all the explorers, knew that an animal shot with a curare-tipped arrow would die in a few moments. But from what? It was obvious that the mere puncture of the arrow would kill nothing. What, then, was in the poison to act so quickly? Could whispers from the jungle provide a clue? Being an expert on the nervous system, he demonstrated a peculiar and valuable attribute of curare which few suspected and no one had ever proved.

He knew, better than most of his colleagues, of the highly complicated impulses transmitted by the brain to all the primary and secondary nerves of the body. These impulses, down to the smallest muscles, dictate muscular activity; without them, muscles would become inactive, flabby or relaxed. He did not try curare on human patients, because at that time it was considered far too dangerous. But, by a series of brilliant experiments on frogs, he proved that curare had a blocking action on impulses from the brain and that animals poisoned by curare lost the normal muscular control of the eyes, lips and, after thorough establishment of the poison in the body, control of the muscles that are essential in respiration. That, of course, explained why death was always caused by asphyxiation.

This discovery merely added to the scientific laurels that were showered on Bernard, but it still left unanswered a number of questions. People were still talking about pot, tube and calabash curare, and much remained to be done before it could become a safe and therapeutic drug for humans.

Back in the jungles of South America botanists and drug hunters were uncovering a lot of information. Some of the Indians were shooting only blowpipe arrows, about fifteen inches long, smeared with curare. These were first definitely reported by Cristobal de Sabedra in 1571. Other Indians used a curare-tipped arrow shot from a bow for killing larger animals. These arrows, some of which are in the writer's study, are about five feet long and have a detachable tip. This, with the poison, is left embedded in the flesh, even if the main arrow is pulled out by a monkey or brushed off as the wounded animal rushes through the jungle. He never rushes very far!

A third type of weapon was a spear used to kill still larger animals, like a tapir or jaguar, the latter usually called a "tiger" in South America. These were of hard wood, the end being very sharp and curare-tipped. All these weapons were used for hunting and in warfare, and some of them are still used in remote parts of curare land. There is a splendid collection of these blowgun darts, of the arrows shot from a bow, and of the spears at the Museu Nacional at Rio de Janeiro.

All this settled the mode of delivery of the poison, but nothing of its constituents. Only much later, in the early part of the present century, did the whole story become available.

The designations of pot, tube and calabash curare had to be abandoned when precise information became available. It was soon clear enough that Indians in Guiana, Venezuela and neighboring regions were using quite different plants from those in Ecuador, Peru and Brazil, over two thousand miles westward. Some were using a species of *Strychnos* of which there are several kinds in South America. From it a curare was made which has the numbing effect on nerve muscles noted by Bernard. This is quite unlike poisoning by strychnine which comes from an Old World relative of the South American plant. Strychnine causes violent convulsions, while curare paralyzes the muscles because it blocks the nervous impulses from the brain.

Other Indians were using very different plants. In the case of *Strychnos,* the poison is extracted only from the outer bark of the tree, the inner bark and wood being discarded. In gathering the other chief source of curare, the natives found that a scrambling woody vine was the most potent. There are several species of these vines, all grouped in the genus *Chondodendron,* and one of the best, *i.e.,* the most poisonous, was *Chondodendron tomentosum.*

Whether from *Strychnos* or *Chondodendron,* the procedure is basically the same. From a crude infusion of the raw poison, curare is boiled down to a gummy mass which will stick to arrows and is much stronger than the raw juice. The next step was to see if enough authentically identifiable curare could be secured for analysis and possible medical use. This was far from easy because while the two main sources of it had been identified, some tribes added other plants, sometimes as many as ten to fifteen. While these have since been proved to be superstitious additions of witch doctors or sorcerers, and many of them were inert, they beclouded the purity of curare for many years.

Finally, as late as 1939, reliable supplies of authentic curare were available, permitting the determination of its active principle and leading the way to its use in medicine. This victory was the result of the combined efforts of botanists, physiologists, pharmacologists, a few intelligent Indians and some white residents of Ecuador and Peru, as well as the pharmaceutical industry.

The paralyzing effect of the drug soon captured the attention of the medical profession. Now that a measured, standardized dose was available, what was it good for? Soon a plethora of papers on curare appeared in the medical press, especially from psychiatrists and neurologists. They well knew that in many institutions for the mentally ill a drastic electric shock treatment was always a hazard, the violence of the effects quite often resulting in broken bones.

It was soon found that curare, in proper doses, would so enervate the muscles of a patient that the electric shock treatment and even the convulsions caused by metrazol were much ameliorated. Perhaps this had been suggested by earlier workers who were already using curare in polio, for children with stiff muscles and even in epileptiforn crises. The theory behind all such treatments was the blocking action of curare upon the normal nerve impulses from the brain to the muscles, just as Bernard had pointed out a hundred years before.

Many other uses of curare have been proposed, most of them of interest only to specialists. But one outstanding contribution of this Indian arrow poison is known to every surgeon. In any abdominal operation, especially with some types of anesthetic, the patient's abdomen often becomes of almost board-like rigidity. Such a condition makes operative procedure quite difficult. It was soon found that an injection of curare would relax the muscles of the abdomen, and that has become standard practice. It began as late as 1942, and surgeons, while demanding relaxation, were alive to the danger of the effects of curare restricting the muscles of respiration.

To guard against this, artificial respiration is always available, and they also have an antidote for curare in a derivative of the calabar bean—neostigmine.

Curare, today, is often replaced by synthetic drugs tailored upon it. There are at least half a dozen such synthetics, some of which are preferred by various surgeons. They are more popular in the United States than in England or on the continent. Years hence it may be possible to evaluate the differences between the synthetics and curare. In the meantime we can be thankful to those South American Indians who quite unwittingly sent a whisper from the earth which turned out to be a very helpful poison.

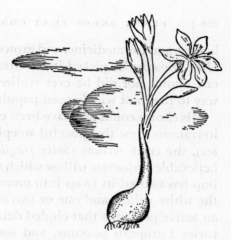

Autumn crocus: the remedy for gout

12. The Pain-Killers

> There is a willow grows aslant a brook,
> That shows his hoar leaves in the glassy stream.
> —*Hamlet.*

ONE OF THE GREATEST MASTERS of medicine was Dioscorides, a fantastically learned Greek physician, who lived some sixteen hundred years before *Hamlet* was written. He knew far more than Shakespeare about the willow with the "hoar leaves." In his monumental *De Materia Medica,* which was the physicians' bible for fifteen hundred years, he wrote of these hoar leaves that "a decoction of them is an excellent fomentation for ye Gout."

This tree was the white willow, now known as *Salix alba,* a native of Eurasia, but having dozens of fairly close relatives the precise identity of which puzzles even the experts. This tree was introduced into America for the making of baskets and for medicine, and grows often up to fifty feet high. How Dioscorides picked it out from all the other willows, no one knows, nor did he ever realize that he was pointing the way to the most widely used popular remedy on earth.

His choice could not have been easy, for all along the Mediterranean grew the graceful weeping willow (*Salix babylonica*), the crack willow (*Salix fragilis*), and the well-nigh unbelievable corkscrew willow which suggests that some irritable imp has twisted its twigs into unnatural spirals. But he chose the white willow and one or two others as the true source of an active principle that eluded detection until 1827. For centuries European peasants, and some of their doctors, were using decoctions or infusions of willow for the pains of gout, rheumatism, neuralgia, toothache, earache or almost any other pain. It was practically never taken internally because willow juice is very bitter, and, of course, no one knew its active ingredient.

The isolation of this baffled the chemists so completely and for so long that the search was practically abandoned. But finally, in 1827, a French chemist, after many failures, told the world that he had isolated the elusive ingredient and appropriately called it *salicin*, a name derived from *Salix*, which had been the proper designation for all the two hundred fifty different kinds of willow ever since the days of the Romans.

Ironically enough, his salicin did not come from a willow. In the hunt for drugs that might have the same properties as the nostrums found in willow, the scientists had screened many other plants. One of them was queen-of-the-meadow, which they called *Spiraea Ulmaria*, but which is now known as *Filipendula Ulmaria*. It is a beautiful, feathery herb, three to five feet high, with tiny white flowers in a showy terminal cluster. It is closely related to the United States queen-of-the-prairie (*Filipendula rubra*) which, however, is taller and has pink flowers. Both are sufficiently showy to be valued garden plants.

It was from the leaves of the queen-of-the-meadow that *salicin* was finally isolated, and this ingredient was soon found in the bark and juice of several species of European willows. But salicin could not be taken internally, and it was hoped that some derivative of it would be of more general use.

In 1838 such a transformation was made by the discovery of salicylic acid, which was made directly from salicin. Here was a refined product, much stronger than the infusions that had been in wide use for eighteen hundred years. But it, also, had one insuperable defect: it could not be taken internally, no matter how severe the pain. This, after a hundred and thirty years, is still so true that the United States federal and state laws forbid its use as a preservative in foods and beverages.

Salicylic acid, however, in spite of this handicap, has become an extremely valuable and very widely used drug for external application. It is one of the absolutely imperative ingredients in the powders sold for so-called athlete's foot, which is an infection of microscopic fungi. It is also widely used in combating dandruff, and in various skin diseases, such as acne. It also has the valuable property of helping in the absorption of other drugs with which it is combined. Without salicylic acid, some of these might be ineffective for lack of absorption through the skin.

We cannot write off salicylic acid as a failure, for besides the uses already mentioned, it has many qualities that the drug compounder finds most useful, as do those people who suffer from an unpleasantly greasy skin (seborrheic dermatitis) or have warts or corns. In spite of its many uses, the chemists never gave up the hunt for some product from willow bark that could be taken internally and that would, they hoped, be a pain-killer of perhaps worldwide use.

Such a quest was crowned with spectacular success when, in Germany, as late as 1899, was evolved *acetylsalicylic acid,* promptly christened *aspirin* by its sponsors and today manufactured in astronomical amounts. They called it aspirin because the German word for its progenitor, salicylic acid, was spirsäure, which commemorated the fact that the father of aspirin had been derived, not from a willow, but from the leaves of what they called *Spiraea Ulmaria.*

A recent check of medical textbooks shows that aspirin is probably more widely prescribed by physicians than almost any other drug. In at least forty different diseases, and in many lesser complaints, the doctors turn to aspirin, primarily as a pain-killer, but also in many other contingencies. Its use by the lay public, much deplored by the medicos, is so huge that one writer guessed that aspirin "is now made by the ton."

Neither aspirin, nor salicylic acid, nor any of their derivatives is now made from willow bark or the leaves of the queen-of-the-meadow, for all of them are produced synthetically and, incidentally, of greater purity than anything derived from natural sources. All are lumped under the general heading of *salicylates,* of which the most important is aspirin —the "wonder drug" of the early years of the twentieth century. It still has amazing popularity both with the profession and the lay public, who take it for every sort of malaise, and often for nothing more serious than boredom or "that tired feeling."

And the public may well be right, for aspirin is the prima donna of drugs. It aims at so many targets, and its aim is often so good, that we delude ourselves into thinking that it has "cured" our trouble, when actually it may be merely a masking palliative. But, the public asks, if it stops the pain of my stiff or creaky joints, isn't that a cure? If that creaky joint is arthritic, aspirin or any other drug will not "cure" the basic trouble, for no one knows either the cause of or the cure for arthritis.

Of what good, then, is aspirin? A complete and correct answer would require a textbook. But certain general principles of its use involve some familiarity with its main targets. Its effectiveness in hitting the very center of them is undisputed, but the mechanism of its action, or how it reaches those targets, is still unknown, or conjectural or disputed.

The public completely ignores such speculations. All they care for is "does it work?" It works so well that some of us may ask what is there in this magical drug that makes it as ubiquitous as bread. One of the important functions of the salicylates is their effect upon the central nervous system, which often helps to reduce body temperature in feverish patients. It does not, on the other hand, reduce the body temperature of normal persons, but especially in highly feverous patients it is widely used, only by physicians and in fairly large doses, to reduce body temperature.

Perhaps more important, because it is so much more prevalent, is the use of aspirin to relieve pain. The pains of headache, earache, joints, neuralgia, and a dozen other instigators of pain are all helped, without, in many cases, the removal or cure of the basic cause of the pain. Its worldwide lay use as a pain-killer should not obscure the fact that it is only about one tenth as effective as morphine. But the use of that drug is dangerous, and it may be criminal, while aspirin in sensible doses is as innocent as tea.

Aspirin has little effect upon the heart and one noted authority, Goodman and Gilman, has written: "There is no clinical or experimental evidence to support the opinion that the salicylates, especially aspirin, are injurious to the heart." This is not showing the green light for wholesale and ignorant dosing of aspirin by the lay public. Far from it, for every year there are many deaths from massive doses of aspirin taken suicidally, or by those in that state of ignorance where if two pills are good, why not take twenty or fifty to speed things up?

Perhaps the most beneficial use of aspirin and some of the other salicylates is to relieve the pain of a peculiarly distressing disease mostly confined to young people. This is rheumatic fever, the early but long-suppressed precursor of many types of heart disease in later life. So common is rheumatic fever that it causes "ten times as many deaths yearly as infantile paralysis." Aspirin is no cure for rheumatic fever, but it helps the doctor to relieve the pain of hot, swollen, red joints and to reduce the fever.

While aspirin and the other salicylates have such a variety of uses, it is their ability to kill pain which puts us all under a lasting debt to the German chemist who had the wit to join the unpalatable salicylic acid with acetic acid. So was born, at the turn of the century, a drug that is now worldwide and whose roots go back eighteen centuries to a Mediterranean willow tree. If Dioscorides was not the first to know that willow juice was a pain-killer, he first put in print that it "is an excellent fomentation for ye Gout."

Gout and the Autumn Crocus

Is gout always the sequel of overindulgence—too much wealth, leisure, women, food and alcohol? It would appear so if we listen to the novelists who picture some belted earl sitting in baronial splendor, sputtering profanity at each twinge of what the doctors call an exquisite pain in his big toe. Exquisite or not, the pain of gout is excruciating, as many know who never expect to be a belted earl.

Ever since the days of Pliny, "gout spread as luxury increased," and one Roman aristocrat suffered its pains for thirty-four years before he committed suicide, in order to live a single day longer than "that brigand Domitian" who was

Emperor of Rome. And Will Durant in *Our Oriental Heritage* wrote that "Kublai Khan had proved his conversion to civilization by developing gout."

The cause of gout is unknown and one recent textbook says, "It has been wrongly ascribed to dietary indiscretions, excessive intake of alcohol, or a sedentary existence." It is often, or perhaps nearly always, associated with an excess of uric acid, and it is ten times as likely to affect men as women. Ever since the days of the *Ebers Papyrus* (around 1500 B.C.) its pains have been so fierce that all the world has cried out for a cure.

It was desperately needed, for gout, while often first attacking the big toe, ultimately spreads to the ankle, instep and knee. One feature that seems almost inhuman is its sudden onset in the middle of the night. One of its most prominent victims was Sir Joseph Banks, the originator of the idea of Kew Gardens.

Somewhere about the sixth or seventh centuries several doctors suggested that hermodactylus was helpful, but few knew what such a drug might be, or where it came from, or exactly how to use it. Later it was found to be the bulb of a Himalayan herb that was ultimately named *Colchicum luteum,* a relative of the much better-known autumn crocus (*Colchicum autumnale*), often called meadow saffron.

Autumn crocus is known to every gardener today, for it is about as showy a fall-blooming bulbous plant as we have. Planted in mid-August, the bulbs produce crocus-like but much larger flowers that spring from the ground in October without any stem or leaves. The flowers, which in some of the modern hybrids are extremely showy, die down before winter, and the following spring, leaves and fruit appear. From this inversion of the usual progression of flowers in the spring and seed in the fall, it acquired the fanciful names of "son before the father," and from its stemless and leafless flowers, "naked ladies."

Few gardeners remember the fact that the autumn crocus, which is not a real crocus and does not even belong to the crocus family, has been known and dreaded for over 2,500 years. In Egypt the bulb (corm) was used for various aches and pains, but with great care, as it was, and still is, violently poisonous. So dangerous is it that Dioscorides in the first century of our era, after carefully describing the autumn crocus, warned of its dangers and was slavishly copied for fifteen centuries.

But the hermodactyl of India, in spite of its poison, had been used by medieval physicians in the treatment of gout, hence why not experiment with the much better-known and closely related autumn crocus? Most doctors were afraid of it, but finally Baron Anton von Storck (1731-1805) in a hospital in Vienna worked out a safe dosage of the crude bulb on experimental animals.

An amusing episode transpired, both in England and in France. With the autumn crocus proved to be almost a specific in gout, two or three "secret" proprietary remedies containing it were put out, usually in wine. The best known was D'Husson's Eau Medicinale, which had a huge sale on the continent and even in England. The *Edinburgh Journal* mentioned "that Sir Joseph Banks, the President of the Royal Society, having experienced the most extraordinary deliverance from his archenemy, made D'Husson's preparation his pocket companion." Not to be outdone by a French nostrum, the British soon concocted "Wilson's Tincture" and "Reynolds' Specific." All of these contained a safe concentration of the crude bulb of autumn crocus (*Colchicum autumnale*).

No one, however, knew what was in the bulb, why it was so poisonous, and how it cured gout. The latter question is still unanswered, as one expert puts it: "It does not relieve other types of pain or inflammation and the mechanism of relief in gout is inexplicable." Finally the active principle in autumn crocus was isolated, named *colchicine* and proved to be such a critical alkaloid that the *United States Pharmacopœia* warns, *"Colchicine is extremely poisonous."*

The measured doses of the pure alkaloid may not be more than 1/120 of a grain, but its effects upon gout are dramatic. Often with one or two doses the horrible pains of gout are dissipated, and some gouty patients carry enough tablets so that if they feel a spasm coming on they take, of course only under the doctor's orders, a sufficient dose to abort the attack. The difference between a helpful and dangerous dose is a little too close for comfort, but the pains of gout are so agonizing that most patients are willing to live between the necessary therapeutic and unquestionably toxic levels that are inherent in these circumstances.

Colchicine has practically no other use. It is completely ineffective in arthritis and rheumatism. Often a doctor may be uncertain if a painful and swollen joint is so because of gout or arthritis. A quick and usual way to settle it is to give the patient a single dose of colchicine. If the pain goes, he has gout; otherwise the diagnosis of arthritis is fairly sure.

Colchicine is also something of a mystery drug. Uric acid concentration is a practically universal concomitant of gout, but colchicine has no demonstrated effect on uric acid, or on its excretion in the urine. It is, therefore, a highly selective and highly successful pain-killer. No one knows why, but gouty people have sung its praises ever since colchicine was extracted from the autumn crocus, that most showy and dangerous of fall-flowering bulbs.

The alkaloid has one final, nonmedical and quite recent use. It was found in Belgium and amply confirmed in the United States that following an injection of colchicine into the ovary of plants, and even if the seeds of plants were treated with it, the effects on the chromosomes were often startling and might be valuable. To exercise a direct effect on such structures was in itself a feat of great scientific interest, and it has been tried on onion (*Allium*), snapdragon (*Antirrhinum*), corn (*Zea*), marigold (*Tagetes*), rubber (*Hevea*), *Datura, Vinca* and many others. If often induces an increase in the number of chromosomes, so that tetraploids are quite often the result.*

The World's Greatest Pain-Killer

Who would seek greater fame than to have rescued Alexander Selkirk from the far-off island of Juan Fernandez on February 2, 1709? London was agog over the rescue and Defoe immortalized it in 1719 by issuing his best-selling *Robinson Crusoe*. Selkirk was picked up by a buccaneer who posed as a privateer, may have been a physician, and whose fame, at least in the medical world, has almost matched the novel.

He was Thomas Dover, and some have called him a quack. However, on that piratical voyage, where many Spanish ships were scuttled, he was in charge of H.M.S. *Duke,* and later invented a remedy ever since known as Dover's powder. This was finally admitted into the *British Pharmacopœia* in 1788, and is even known today all over Europe and in the United States.

Dover called his remedy a diaphoretic, which merely means that it promotes perspiration. The most important of its ingredients would certainly induce sweating, as the dose was the astounding amount of 100 grains. If this seems a bit excessive, the apothecaries were quick to chide Dover about it. He facetiously advised patients "to make their wills before

* For an explanation of these genetic concepts the reader may consult question #446 in the writer's book entitled, *1001 Questions Answered About Flowers*, Dodd, Mead & Co., 1963.

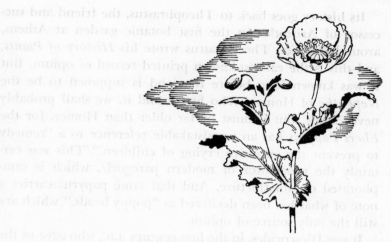

Opium poppy, the only source of morphine

they venture upon so large a dose." The powder was taken in a glass of wine before retiring, when many of the patients had so much pain that they could not put a foot to the floor.

But Dover promised "they would walk next day," and most of them did. Of course curiosity flared up all over England as to the constituents of such a quick cure. He made no secret of its ingredients and published the formula. It had at least five, ipecac among them, but most of them could be ignored. The only really important ingredient was opium, the greatest pain-killer the world has ever known.

Many wondered how Dover knew enough to concoct such a remedy. His medical education, if he had any, is completely unknown. He did, however, have one considerable advantage. As a very young man he lived in the house of Sir Thomas Sydenham, the most famous physician in seventeenth-century England and often called "The English Hippocrates." That great doctor knew all there was to know about opium, including its ancient and fabulous history.

Its history goes back to Theophrastus, the friend and successor of Aristotle. In the first botanic garden at Athens, around 300 B.C., Theophrastus wrote his *History of Plants,* and this is the earliest-known printed record of opium. But it was known long before that and is supposed to be the *Nepenthe* of Homer. Who first found it, we shall probably never know, but it must be far older than Homer, for the *Ebers Papyrus* has an unmistakable reference to a "remedy to prevent the excessive crying of children." This was certainly the progenitor of modern paregoric, which is camphorated opium tincture. And that same papyrus carries a note of what has been decifered as "poppy heads," which are still the only source of opium.

It was Dioscorides, in the first century A.D., who gave us the first description of how opium was derived from "poppy heads." His account cannot be improved upon, and exactly the same tactics are used today. A few days after the petals fall from the opium poppy plant, there develops a greenish pod about two inches high and nearly as thick. When still quite unripe, this pod is delicately slit with a many-bladed knife. The cuts must not puncture the pod or touch the seeds within it. From these shallow cuts exudes a milky juice the coagulation of which is fairly rapid. This coagulated mass is crude opium. Sometimes the pod may be slit for the second or third time, so long as milky juice continues to flow. By an extraordinary alchemy of nature, the seeds within the pod are completely innocuous and are widely used to sprinkle on rolls.

But all the world has known for thousands of years that opium is far from innocuous, and that while it may be the world's greatest pain-killer, it is one of the most dangerous— not because it is an active poison that kills quickly, but because it lulls the senses against the dangers of addiction.

The opium poppy, christened *Papaver somniferum* by the immortal Linnaeus in 1753, was well named by the father of botany, for he knew that, of all the poppies, it was the only one that would produce "the sleep of endless reverie." It is an annual plant, three to five feet high, a native of Asia Minor but now grown throughout the warmer parts of the world—often illicitly. Its cultivation is forbidden in the United States, while its close relatives, the perennial oriental poppy (*Papaver orientale*), the Iceland poppy (*Papaver nudicaule*) and the corn poppy (*Papaver Rhoeas*), are in every garden. Not one of these is of any medicinal value.

It was the sleep-producing quality of opium that first attracted the attention of the ancients. When the plant was taken from Asia Minor to Greece, they coined the word *Opium,* which is merely a Greek word for juice, for they well knew that opium was the coagulated juice of the "poppy heads." Even today that gummy exudate is almost exactly the same as the Greeks knew it, and American manufacturers face the same rascally adulterants as were found by the ancients. Sticks, stones, gravel, and the seeds of other plants all are easy to hide in the gummy mass and the growers often sophisticate opium with such adulterants. The United States Government now restricts opium importation to that containing 9.5 per cent of morphine by weight.

The ancients had no such protection, for the very existence of morphine in opium eluded detection for eighteen hundred years after crude opium was in wide use in Greece, Rome and all along the Mediterranean. Arabian traders carried opium and its seeds to Persia and China, with disastrous results. Marco Polo records its use in Persia in the thirteenth century and an old Chinese proverb reminds us of its effects:

If you have a bitter enemy, whom you wish to destroy, there is no need to fight him, steal his wife or stab at night in a dark corner; the best thing you can do is to invite him to smoke opium and let the drug do the rest.*

The legitimate medical use of opium by the ancients is so well authenticated it scarcely needs discussion. Dioscorides even published a warning of its dangers:

A little of it, taken as much as a grain of Ervum [probably the ervil, a vetch], is a pain-easer and a sleep-causer, and a digester, . . . but being drank too much it hurts, making men lethargical and it kills.

For a first-century physician there could scarcely be a better description of its use and danger. A century later, the great Galen, physician to Marcus Aurelius, wrote on opium. He also published his ninety-eight medical books. He and Dioscorides, the flowers of Greek medicine, shared the unprecedented honor of dictating medical practice for the next fifteen hundred years.

Opium was also well known to the galaxy of Arabian doctors of the ninth and tenth centuries, culminating in the towering figure of Avicenna. This learned Arab, who spent much time in Persia, was the outstanding Mohammedan physician. He lived in a palace in the magical city of Isfahan, was a bit of a rake and kept a bevy of concubines.

Raw or crude opium was the only product of the poppy available to the doctors for over two thousand years. The small pieces of gummy exudate were far from palatable and, like so many crude drugs, intensely bitter. That is why Dioscorides prepared his "syrup of opium" to relieve pain and induce sleep, anticipating by sixteen hundred years Shakespeare's Othello and his "drowsy syrups."

In the early fifteen hundreds there burst upon the Euro-

* This book does not deal with the narcotic action of opium or any of its derivatives, nor with addiction to such drugs. Those interested in this may find it in the writer's *Narcotics: Nature's Dangerous Gifts*, Dell Publishing Co., 1963.

pean medical world a meteoric, unstable genius, bombastic, drunk most of the time, but a definite milestone in the history of opium. He was Philipus Aureolus Theophrastus Bombastus von Hohenheim, a name he abandoned for Paracelsus. When he arrived to take the job as professor at the University of Basel, he began the course by burning in a chafing dish, to the consternation of his colleagues and students, the books of Theophrastus, Dioscorides, Galen and Avicenna. The only book he saved was by Hippocrates, the Greek "father of medicine," who apparently had no knowledge of opium.

After the burning, Paracelsus explained that he was more learned than any of the ancients, and also denounced the ignorance of all the apothecaries. Not unnaturally he was far from popular, and after a rather rancid lawsuit he "found it advisable to leave Basel hurriedly." But he later practiced all over Europe, and after the Swiss fiasco published the formula for *laudanum,* a name he may have invented. It was a mixture of opium and alcohol, now called tincture of opium, but as laudanum it was the drug that so disastrously enslaved De Quincey, Elizabeth Barrett Browning and Coleridge. Just before his death the latter wrote:

After my death, I earnestly entreat that a full and unqualified narrative of my wretchedness, and of its guilty cause, may be made public, that at least some little good may be effected by the direful example.

In spite of such tragic abuse, tincture of opium became a standard drug all over Europe long before the British addicts made it notorious. There was then no other drug that could compare with it to relieve pain and produce sleep. Some idea of its popularity can be gained by the announcement in 1680 by Sir Thomas Sydenham, then the leading physician in England:

Among the remedies which it has pleased Almighty God to give to man to relieve his sufferings, none is so universal and so efficacious as opium.

That is still true today, not with opium, but with the extraordinary battery of alkaloids that have been extracted from this magical juice of the pods of the opium poppy. The very word *alkaloid* was, of course, completely unknown to Sydenham and was just as complete a mystery for the next one hundred twenty-three years. Many scientists wondered what the active principle of opium could be, but no answer came until 1803 and then from a small pharmacy in Paderborn, Westphalia, Germany.

The discoverer was a youth of twenty, apprenticed to a pharmacist in Paderborn at the age of sixteen. He was Frederich Wilhelm Adam Sertürner, who was born at Neuhaus, June 19, 1783. In his spare time at the pharmacy he had been working on opium, so much so that he accumulated notes on nearly sixty separate experiments in an attempt to isolate the active ingredient. Finally, in 1803, he succeeded not only in isolating that ingredient, but discovered that it was an *alkaloid,* a substance unknown and even undreamed of at that time.

The alkaloid that he extracted from opium he subsequently named *morphium,* which is now the worldwide drug *morphine.* To have discovered the nature of an alkaloid and to have isolated morphine in the process would have entitled him to the Nobel Prize if one had existed then. One of his biographers has written, "Sertürner's discovery stands well alongside of the greatest discoveries which have benefited the human race."

Quite apart from his spectacular achievement, Sertürner touched off a huge amount of research on other possible plant alkaloids. It is impossible here to list them all, but a few of the most important were strychnine (1817), quinine (1820), caffeine (1820), nicotine (1828), atropine (1833) and cocaine (1855). Until the young German pharmacist pointed the way, all these drugs were known only in their crude form, and none of them, including opium, could be prescribed with anything like the accuracy that Sertürner had made possible.

He was, of course, hailed all over Europe as a genius, but he had his detractors and imitators. A couple of French chemists claimed that they had isolated morphine about the time of or even before Sertürner. Much acrimonious dispute ensued, but it was finally decided that their end product was not morphine, and to clinch the matter the Institute of France voted a prize of two thousand francs to Sertürner and a citation that it was given him "for having recognized the basic nature of morphine and for having discovered a method which had produced great medical discoveries."

It is impossible to exaggerate the importance of this, and no honor was adequate to compensate such a genius, for he literally revolutionized medical practice. Here for the first time in history a doctor could prescribe a measured dose of a pure alkaloid. It would be pleasant to say good-by to Sertürner upon the assumption that he would retire to an honored old age. Actually, after he moved to Einbeck, he "made many flights into fields where he had no special or even moderate competence." These brought him much criticism and even ridicule, and he died at fifty-seven, a bitter and a disappointed genius. Nevertheless, he will always be among the immortals.

The isolation of morphine opened up a new world of research. Not too long after 1820 it was found that morphine was only one of about twenty alkaloids in opium. Only two others are of much medical significance, but these are outstanding: *codeine,* which was named for the Greek word for poppy head, and *papaverine,* so called from *Papaver,* the generic name of all the poppies. Of these three, morphine is by far the most important.

Its actions on the human body are manifold. Its most useful attribute comes from its direct effect upon the central nervous system. This is manifested at first by the loss of the sense of pain, either from injuries, as in battle, or from disease. So marked is this that relief will come in about sixty minutes from an oral dose, but in much less time after a hypodermic injection. The effects are magical, and pain, as such, is under the control of the physician, with a measured dose of morphine. For some unexplained reason it has no effect on the lightning-like pains in locomotor ataxia (tabes dorsalis), but its place as a pain-killer is otherwise absolutely unrivaled.

It has, too, a simultaneous action besides easing our pains, for it is also a stimulant. This apparent anomaly is explained by the pharmacologist as its double action. Its pain-killing mechanism resides in the brain and the nerves sparked by it. But morphine is definitely a spinal stimulant. It is the latter that makes the patient pleasantly drowsy, muscularly relaxed, free of anxiety, intellectually alert; and usually his fears, doubts and inhibitions evaporate quickly. It is, of course, these attributes that appeal to the addicts, and it is this temporary stimulant effect that crooked trainers use when horses doped with morphine win a race they might otherwise lose. Many tracks in the United States and in England have been charged with this tampering with horses. Perhaps some of the trainers know how old this is. For centuries Arabs were feeding opium to the fleetest horses in the world.

The ultimate effect of morphine, after its wonderful obliteration of pain and the other qualities mentioned above, is to induce a dreamless sleep. That's why it was named morphine after the God of Sleep, Morpheus—the legendary deity always shown "with a poppy plant in his hand." It was this euphoria, followed by a marvelously dreamless slumber, that made De Quincey call opium "The Abyss of Divine Enjoyment."

For two thousand years the doctors and addicts who used opium, without any notion of its ingredients, were actually absorbing morphine, as modern studies reveal the fact that nearly all opium contains from 9 to 12 per cent of morphine. Its combination of killing pain, producing euphoria and final sleep made this drug one of the most important of all the specifics derived from plants. Its use among patients with terminal cancer has made their final death, if not absolutely painless, as nearly so as possible. No wonder Sir William Osler repeated many times that "Morphine was God's own Medicine."

It has, however, several drawbacks. It decreases respiration, often alarmingly so in overdoses, and there is the constant danger of addiction. That is why most careful doctors will not tell the patient that the relief of his pains is due to morphine, or even to one of its synthetic substitutes, of which there are now several. Also morphine tends to make the patient constipated, give him pinpoint pupils, and has several other undesirable effects, none of which, with ordinary therapeutic doses, is sufficiently troublesome to warrant abandonment of the drug and most of which can be corrected by suitable methods.

No doctor would dream of giving up morphine, for besides its great pain-killing properties it has too many other uses. Recent checks of medical texts disclose that physicians use morphine in over forty diseases or complaints. Scarcely any other drug can compare with it in its wide application.

Somewhat less used, but still of very extensive medical value, is the second alkaloid of opium, known as *codeine,* which was first isolated in 1832. Every householder knows that the best of cough syrups contain codeine. He may not know that its pain-killing properties are about one fifth those of morphine, that it is less likely to lead to addiction and because of its safety is widely used in over thirty different diseases, among them laryngitis, dysmenorrhea, mumps, whooping cough, neuritis and in that most ubiquitous of all diseases, the common cold.

The third, and only other medically important alkaloid of opium is *papaverine,* first isolated in 1848. Its uses are more selective than either morphine or codeine is, but its value is appreciated by physicians for the few diseases in which it is effective. It has no narcotic effect, does not ease pain and there is little or no danger of addiction. Its actions on the central nervous system are negligible, but its effects on increasing blood flow are dramatic. Cases are on record where, following its use, limbs threatened with amputation because of loss of blood flow and impending gangrene were completely relieved and adequate blood flow restored in a matter of minutes. It is thus, and in acute emergencies, life-saving. Other examples of its use are in Buerger's disease, angina pectoris and in other afflictions of the heart.

The last and most notorious of all the alkaloids of opium is *heroin.* It is used today only by drug addicts, as its manufacture and importation into the United States, even for medical purposes, is forbidden. It has somewhat the same clinical uses as morphine, but greatly increases the euphoria, for which the addicts take it. The illicit manufacture and importation is so great that an official of the United States Narcotic Bureau testified:

If you had the Army, the Navy, the Coast Guard, the F.B.I., the Customs Service and our own Service [the United States Narcotic

Bureau], you would not stop heroin coming through the Port of New York.

For the better part of three thousand years opium farmers have wondered about the capsule of the opium poppy. Much later, plant physiologists and pharmacologists joined in that wonderment. For only about eight to ten days of its young life does the immature capsule exude the milky juice that becomes opium. And only then if it is very carefully slit. At this juncture, and at no other time, does this magical juice contain about twenty alkaloids—morphine, codeine and papaverine among them—all highly complicated chemically.

Hardly any vagary of nature is so mystifying, for the mature pod, which is allowed to ripen after the extraction is finished, contains no opium, and the seeds within it are entirely innocuous. Besides being sprinkled on rolls, these seeds contain a perfectly safe, palatable oil, much used to adulterate olive oil!

To complicate the problem still further, nearly 75 per cent of raw opium consists of relatively worthless and completely inert waxes, resins and other useless ingredients. But from that precious 25 per cent of residue has been extracted, thanks to Sertürner, the greatest pain-killer in the world.

The merest amateur botanist can easily record the above facts, but it would take a botanical Einstein to answer the age-old questions of How? and Why? If we turn to the plant physiologists, they give us a vast elaboration of the process, but at this writing no real answer as to why, for only about ten days, a particular poppy plant secretes a special kind of juice that has become what Sir William Osler called it— "God's own Medicine."

Not all plants of the opium poppy yield the desired amount of it. There are today several varieties or strains grown in

Macedonia, Bulgaria, Yugoslavia, Egypt, Iran and India. Some of these opiums are imported, but still most opium, and the finest, comes from where it is conjectured the opium poppy was originally native. This is the land of the ancient Hittites in Asia Minor, and today our best opium is Turkish, exported from the port of Smyrna, now called Izmir.

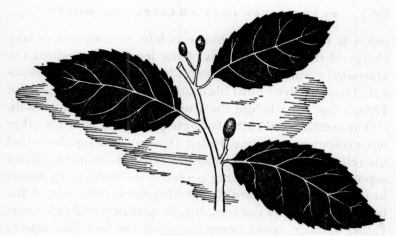

Chaulmoogra: ancient remedy for leprosy

13. Father Damien, Stevenson, and Joseph F. Rock

NOT MANY REMEMBER and only a few have ever heard of the uproar caused by Stevenson's "An Open Letter to the Rev. Dr. Hyde." This Presbyterian divine had "issued some ill-considered imputations upon Father Damien," who was an heroic Roman Catholic priest fighting a losing battle against a disease that finally killed him. Stevenson and the rest of the world were outraged that anyone could impute base motives to a man who gave his life to help the pitiful unfortunates who were isolated on an island in Hawaii because they had an incurable and loathsome disease.

Father Damien, whose real name was Joseph de Veuster, was born in Belgium in 1840, and went as a missionary to the "Pacific Islands" in 1863. The next year he was ordained a priest at Honolulu, and nine years later volunteered to take charge of the spiritual needs of the leper colony which the Hawaiian government had established on the island of Molokai. There he lived until his death from leprosy on April 15, 1889, a few years before the United States annexed Hawaii.

The conditions on Molokai were just as bad as in any other leper colony at that time. Father Damien soon supplemented his religious duties with practical ones like housing, water supply, sanitation and other necessary facilities. Help flowed in from all over the world, and Molokai became one of the best of all the leper colonies. But in spite of worldwide fame, Father Damien could never overcome the fact that leprosy was a particularly loathsome disease of which the cause was then unknown. Nor was there any real cure, except more or less vague rumors of a remedy from tropical Asia.

Almost from the beginning of recorded history, leprosy has been a slow, insidious and frightful disease from which everyone fled. Before leper colonies were established, the victims became shunned outcasts, usually poverty-stricken, ragged, dirty and forced to wear a bell so that the healthy could avoid them. Today there are millions of people in warm damp climates infected with leprosy, not all of them safely isolated. There is even one small leper colony in Louisiana, maintained by the United States government; but there are huge ones in the Philippines, India, Africa and Malaya. In such places there is no real cure for advanced cases, but science holds out such hope for early detected cases that the whole picture has changed for the better since the turn of the century.

Even as early as 1874, just after Father Damien went to Molokai, Dr. G. A. Hansen, a Norwegian physician, discovered for the first time that leprosy was caused by a bacterium which was named *Mycobacterium leprae*. Such are the age-

old and horrible connotations of *leprosy* that many doctors
and patients now call the affliction Hansen's disease.

By whatever name, few diseases are so horrible, and practically all advanced and untreated cases are fatal. Death often
comes many years after the first infection, which may go un-
detected for a long time. At first there is an almost unnoticed
lack of sensitivity of the skin, which as the disease progresses
comes to a stage where cuts or a bruise cause little if any pain.
Later the skin becomes mottled with red, purple or bronze
spots, from one-half to four and one-half inches wide, among
which are yellow or reddish-brown nodules. Eyebrows fall off
and facial deformity becomes obvious, including nasal ulcers.
There is often fever and in later stages there is so much disturbance of the nervous system that extremities become ener-
vated and ultimately fingers and toes drop off. Such advanced
and very infective cases may live for many years.

As to the method of transmission of leprosy, there is still
some obscurity. All the authorities appear to agree that it is
most easily caught by skin contact. Hence no infected person
should ever sleep in the same bed with an uninfected one.
This sounds simple enough, but is actually very difficult in
crowded and often unsanitary native huts.

It is no wonder that such a frightful disease should set the
doctors to work hunting for a cure. This has been going on
ever since the first leprosy case was found in the Nile Valley
perhaps 2,500 years ago. But with no certain knowledge of
what caused it and with the terror of infection, the remedies
were fear-inspired and practically valueless. Notwithstanding
these failures, the seeds of a few trees in India and southeast
Asia had been used by the natives for centuries as a remedy
for Hansen's disease, and quite obviously ignored by the rest
of the world until 1853.

At that time a doctor in the British Indian Medical Service
listened to two ancient documents on the remedy for leprosy

—one Chinese, the other Hindu. Perhaps a thousand years ago the Hindu document contained the statement that:

Chaulmoogra oil is very efficacious in leprosy. It is given in doses of ten to twenty drops after meals and it is also used externally on the affected parts. The treatment is to be continued for at least three months.

The Chinese document was even older, for the Emperor Shen Nung mentioned the same oil in his reputed pharmacopoeia, written before 2500 B.C. But modern medicine practically ignored these statements, perhaps because the crude oil was rather nauseating and there was considerable uncertainty as to how it was obtained and from what. A British investigator in 1904 devised a method of making the oil a little more palatable and useful, but it added nothing to the question of where chaulmoogra oil came from and how it was extracted.

That riddle was solved by a truly remarkable Austrian botanist, born in Vienna on January 13, 1884, and christened Joseph F. Rock. Early in his youth he was enamored of tales of far-off lands and the language used in such places. An example of his interest came when he was only ten years old, and his father took him to Egypt. He picked up enough Arabic so that at sixteen he was teaching that language at the university in Vienna. His father hoped that he would study for the priesthood, but Rock instead wandered around Europe and at Antwerp decided to spend the summer in England. Missing the channel steamer, he impulsively sailed for New York, where he arrived on September 9, 1905, already fluent in Arabic, German, French and Spanish, but weak in English. His health drove him to the drier climate of Texas where, to improve his English, he went to the University. He became an American citizen in 1913 and subsequently all his writings were in English. Against his doctor's orders, he went to Hawaii in 1907, and started on a meteoric career which ultimately solved the chaulmoogra riddle.

Due to the refinement of chaulmoogra oil in England, the demand for it had so increased that there seemed no hope of adequate supplies. The late Dr. David Fairchild, then head of the Division of Foreign Seed and Plant Introduction of the United States Department of Agriculture, determined to do something about it. Due to Rock's spectacular achievements in the tropical botany of the Pacific Islands, Dr. Fairchild chose him to go to what was then called Indo-China and also to Siam, Burma and India to investigate the trees that were the assumed source of chaulmoogra oil.

He landed at Singapore in 1920, and went by rail to Bangkok. He already knew Chinese, and was aware that the trees belonged to a family of plants known as Flacourtiaceae, which are exclusively tropical. The only well-known species in the United States is the kei-apple from South Africa, grown in Florida and southern California for its fruit. Rock also knew the well-hashed story of a legendary king of India who not only cured his leprosy with chaulmoogra, but found a leprous maiden in the forest, cured and married her. Rock was never married and had the proper amount of skepticism for such fictional fancies. He was after facts, and he obtained them.

It would take up far too much space to recount Rock's adventures in these countries, his bouts with jungle fever, malaria, bandits, communists, tigers, rapids and other hazards. What he was seeking was the exact identity of chaulmoogra trees and a supply of authentic seeds for germination in Hawaii, as no part of the continental United States is suited to them.

After incredible difficulties, it simmered down to three different trees, all belonging to the Flacourtiaceae. They became so important that we record the pertinent details:

1. *Hydnocarpus wightiana.* A tall Indian tree with leathery leaves, large white flowers, and a hairy fruit in the pulp of which are embedded many seeds. It is the oil extracted from these seeds which is now called Hydnocarpus oil (otherwise chaulmoogra oil).
2. *Hydnocarpus anthelmintica.* A closely related tree from Burma and Assam, also a source of Hydnocarpus oil.
3. *Taraktogenos kurzi.* A related tree, but not so important a source of oil as the other two.

Rock found that the seeds of all three trees were sold in the native markets for the extraction of oil, and because the oil from all of them is so similar, it was admitted into the next to the last edition of the *United States Pharmacopœia* as chaulmoogra oil. Today, only the first two species are accredited as a proper source of oil, and it is called by the experts Hydnocarpus oil, although millions of lepers and their doctors use the much better-known term of chaulmoogra oil for this immense blessing.

Rock also found that the seeds are crushed and pressed, without heat, to extract the oil, which is clear, yellowish and rather acrid. One native use of the seeds was to stupefy fish, but for centuries in southeast Asia and in India its chief use was as a remedy for leprosy. Rock sent abundant seed to Hawaii, where a large plantation of the trees was started to assure future seed supply. The tree does not begin to bear seeds until eight to ten years from planting.

This solver of botanical riddles became so enamored of things Chinese that he spent nearly thirty years after his chaulmoogra triumph in the region near the Chinese frontier of Tibet. Thousands of plants and birds of this little-known area were sent to museums and botanic gardens all over the world. And to top off his career, he became so fluent in the dialects of these tribes that he put into English over eight thousand books heretofore unavailable because they were in

Na-khi language. Only the Chinese communists finally drove him back to Hawaii, where he was buried on December 10, 1962, at the age of seventy-nine.

The availability of chaulmoogra oil changed the whole picture of treating leprosy in the huge institutions devoted to these unfortunates. The oil is not a cure for advanced cases, but for many incipient ones it has remarkable value. Thousands of young sufferers from leprosy used to avoid the stigma of being an inmate of a leprosarium to such an extent that they never went there. Most of these were in the early stages of the disease, completely noninfective, but without treatment, inevitably headed for a long, lingering hideous illness ending years hence in death.

Thousands of such early-stage cases are now voluntarily going to such institutions because they know that, in the vast majority of cases, the result is a complete cure and that they will ultimately be discharged to their homes completely non-infective. Such a course of treatment takes from three to five years, but who would not spare that time to be rid of the infection instead of facing the dread alternatives?

Chaulmoogra oil, in spite of its miraculous qualities, has a few disadvantages. It is inclined to be nauseating and even rejected at times. Taken by mouth, as it used to be, and for long periods, it often upsets the digestive tract, and the treatment has to be interrupted. This led to injections of the oil, but these are often painful, and treatment may have to consist of alternate injections and the taking of the drug by mouth. Furthermore, chaulmoogra oil is rather expensive. These disadvantages led the drug seekers to find something better than chaulmoogra oil, in spite of its great value and long history.

Perhaps the hunt for the *perfect* treatment of leprosy is one of the finest illustrations of the helpful co-operation between synthetic chemists, pharmacologists, physicians and botanists like Rock, who seek drugs from the plant world.

These experts combine their talents to conquer a disease that has been rampant for centuries. As other chapters of this book have shown, there has always been a friendly rivalry between those scientists who seek healing drugs from plants and those who begin in the laboratory and end up with a purely synthetic drug. Such chemists have to solve many technical puzzles and continue work in spite of many failures.

Chaulmoogra, of course, was a completely plant drug, and its great value and disadvantages were known to all. It was the latter that sparked the chemical investigations that ultimately, and only within the last few years, produced a synthetic drug that many experts think is better than chaulmoogra oil. It did not come into use for leprosy until the middle of the 1940's, and for a peculiar reason. The drug had been tailor-made in the laboratory for helping those suffering from tuberculosis, but it proved unsatisfactory in that disease.

It had always been known that there was some resemblance between the insidious progress of tuberculosis and leprosy, in spite of the fact that they were caused by very different organisms, and that their ultimate sequelae were so unlike. At any rate, because of the technical resemblance between the two diseases, the new drug was tried in leprosy, and has almost supplanted chaulmoogra oil in the treatment of that disease.

The new cure is a derivative of the sulfa drugs that are still widely used in a variety of other diseases. But the new leprosy cure was tried first in 1946 at the leprosarium in Louisiana and in many other institutions. There are several forms of the drug, all generically called sulfones, one of the most useful being *sulfoxone sodium,* which was admitted into the latest edition of the *United States Pharmacopœia,* from which chaulmoogra was deleted.

These sulfone drugs have revolutionized leprosy treatment

in nearly all first-class leprosariums. Like chaulmoogra, they can be given by mouth or injection and the results are so favorable that most of the experts think that patients, after a long course of treatment, can be discharged as completely noninfective. One huge leprosarium in the Philippines has been able to discharge nearly 50 per cent of its patients, leaving only the advanced older cases, for whom there is little hope.

These sulfones also have some disadvantages. Like chaulmoogra, they must be given for protracted periods, and in some patients cause various side reactions such as a form of anemia, bloody urine, nausea and a skin rash. None of these has made it necessary to stop treatment, and an interruption of it usually clears up these undesirables.

Whether the sulfones will ever completely replace chaulmoogra is a question that only time will reveal. At present in many underdeveloped countries the plant product still has a wide use. And Sir Leonard Rogers, a British physician, has stated that a combined treatment of chaulmoogra and sulfones is better than either of them used separately.

If Sir Leonard's prediction turns out to be correct, it may well be the final answer to a very old question: Is leprosy curable? Taken in its early stages, it certainly appears to be, for thousands of patients have been discharged as completely cured and incapable of infecting anyone. That is a tremendous victory, and if we were honoring the victors, perhaps a fair share of the laurels should crown the heads of the synthetic chemists and also the late Joseph F. Rock.

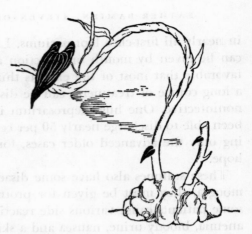

A Mexican yam that yields hormones

14. Thomas Addison and Two Tropical Plants

DR. THOMAS ADDISON, a Scottish physician, was graduated from the medical school of the University of Edinburgh in 1816 with no indication that he would ultimately become world-famous. That did not come until 1855, when he was on the staff of the old and much-revered Guy's Hospital in London. There he had many patients, some of whom had a variety of symptoms, the cause of which was then quite unknown, although the outcome was always fatal.

All these patients had what Addison described as "anemia, general languor and debility, remarkable feebleness of the heart's action, irritability of the stomach, and a peculiar change of colour in the skin." At autopsy he could find no organs such as the heart, liver, lungs or kidneys that either separately or together were the obvious cause of the illness or of its fatal outcome. He then found that the disease was always "occurring in connection with a diseased condition of the 'supra-renal capsules.' " That was his name for what we now known as the adrenal glands, and the affliction has ever since been known as Addison's disease, which is fortunately rather rare, and no longer necessarily fatal, due to developments that would have amazed Dr. Addison.

The adrenal glands had been known ever since the sixteenth century, and several incorrect theories of their use had been advanced, but it was Addison who first suggested that the diseased condition of the glands was the cause of the death of his patients. That discovery induced much research by Charles Brown-Sequard, a French-American physician born on the island of Mauritius but doing much of his work at Harvard and in Paris. He first demonstrated that life was impossible soon after the adrenal glands were removed from experimental animals. Since his time, their function has been so much explored and so enormously elaborated that the results have hit the Stock Exchange.

While death was certain without them, it took a vast amount of work to find out just what the adrenal glands actually did. That a pair of glands just above the kidneys could be important seemed fantastic, considering their small size—about two inches long. But it was soon found that they secreted *hormones,* and that some of these "chemical messengers" have tremendous power in regulating our daily life, especially those secreted by the outer envelope of the gland, known today as adrenal cortical hormones. That medical trilogy means literally hormones secreted by the cortex (outer envelope) of the adrenal gland.

That these glands contained hitherto unsuspected properties has been known ever since the turn of this century. At that time a hormone secreted by the interior (medulla) of

the adrenal gland had been isolated and even made synthetically and named epinephrine, but now often called adrenalin.
Its action on blood pressure and the heart, as well as other
benefits, has ever since made adrenalin a standard remedy.

But adrenalin is secreted naturally only in the medulla (interior) of the adrenal gland, and it is the hormones secreted by
the outer envelope (cortex) that have more recently captured
the attention of all pharmacologists and every pharmaceutical manufacturer in America, as well as the highly important ones in England, Holland, Germany, France, Switzerland and Italy. Competition is so keen and so very expensive
that millions of dollars have been spent in the synthesis and
production of the hormones originally isolated from the cortex of the adrenal glands. These were once and by some
are still called the supra-renal glands because they lie immediately above the kidneys.

The study of these cortical hormones has filled volumes,
for over thirty adrenocortical hormones have been isolated
from the cortex, and some of them are of worldwide significance. The ones that chiefly concern us here are cortisone, its
derivatives, analogues and related hormones.

The chemical composition of these hormones is so complicated that only highly trained organic chemists can master
the technique of their isolation, let alone their manufacture.
Cortisone is no exception, and until fairly recently it was
simply one of the many hormones secreted by the cortex of
the adrenal gland. The latter is one of the ductless glands of
the body the study of which comprises endocrinology, or the
functions of endocrines, i.e., glands of internal secretion.
Among others are the pituitary and thyroid glands.

Cortisone was finally isolated at the Mayo Clinic as late as
1934 by Dr. E. C. Kendall and his associates, and called at
first Kendall's Compound E. Several European investigators
also announced the isolation of cortisone at about the same

time. Its therapeutic qualities were not then well known and at first it was considered simply as one of the hormones secreted by the outer envelope (cortex) of the adrenal gland. That immeasurably important cortex varies from only 0.01 to 0.04 of an inch thick!

While the isolation of cortisone was a highly creditable chemical feat, it told us next to nothing as to the uses it could be put to, or how to make it available. Its availability posed no problem at first, for it was used chiefly on experimental animals. But in 1938 it was noticed at the Mayo Clinic that patients with rheumatoid arthritis suffered less if they were pregnant or had certain forms of jaundice.

The doctors speculated as to what connection there might be between pregnancy, jaundice and the reduction of arthritis. They finally wondered if an adrenocortical hormone (cortisone) might be effective.

A single patient with crippling rheumatoid arthritis was chosen for the trial, and under cortisone therapy the improvement was rapid and striking. Later tests on many more patients sustained the original findings and cortisone, in irresponsible newspapers and sensational magazines, burst upon the world as a "cure" for arthritis. It has no such value, but it and its derivatives and analogues have worldwide use in ameliorating the crippling state of arthritic patients, and for many other diseases. But it is not a cure for arthritis, as it was once supposed to be.

Medical statistics reveal that there are about three million cases of severe rheumatoid arthritis in the United States and perhaps as many more who are not yet so advanced in the disease, the cause of which is still unknown, as is any permanent cure. The misery and pain of rheumatoid arthritis are so great, however, that when the work at the Mayo Clinic finally filtered down to the general practitioners and internists, the demand for cortisone reached astronomic proportions in the United States and throughout Europe. The minute amounts used by the Mayo doctors were essential, even if cortisone at that time cost about one hundred dollars a gram (15 grains), so precious was this rare substance and so difficult to come by.

It had long been known that cattle, hogs and sheep also have adrenal glands, and it was found that the bile, urine and other products of these animals contain the starting materials from which organic chemists could produce cortisone. But the process was also costly, difficult, and it had, at first, an almost insuperable handicap. From a single ox weighing perhaps one thousand pounds the yield of this starting material was so small that it would take forty such animals to produce enough cortisone to treat one patient for a single day.

That extraction technique has since been improved, but its difficulty and cost set up a chain reaction all over the world to find a cheap and unlimited supply of a material that would ensure the future of cortisone, its derivatives and especially its analogues, which were to burst upon the world much later and much more violently.

The Plant That Failed

Cortisone and most of the hormones originating in the adrenal cortex have been thoroughly analyzed chemically and found to contain steroids; hence the common name for these products of research and manufacture is "steroid drugs." For most of us *steroid*, as a term, is a bit difficult to define. The best available definition is in Dr. Applezweig's *Steroid Drugs*, which says, in part, "Steroids are organic molecules, . . . so named because they are related to, and in most cases derived from, sterols which are found abundantly in nature . . . , usually in animal and plant fats."

The realization of this touched off a worldwide hunt for

plants that might contain steroids and hence be the starting material for the manufacture of cortisone. The extraction of that hormone from animal sources involved at least thirty-two chemical steps—difficult and expensive. But the botanists had not been idle, and the hunt for plants was finally rewarded by an announcement in 1929 that all but escaped attention, for it then seemed to have no bearing on the cortisone problem.

In that year Drs. Walter A. Jacobs and Michael Heidelberger published a paper on "Sarmentocymarin and Sarmentogenin" which disclosed the fact that an African vine produced seeds containing these substances and that the vine was a species of *Strophanthus*. It was for long suspected that the source of the material described by Jacobs and Heidelberger was *Strophanthus sarmentosus*. Hence their name sarmentogenin, which signifies that the source was that plant and that it contained one of the sapogenins, now known to be promising materials for the ultimate conversion into cortisone.

Furthermore, *Strophanthus* was well known to the experts as the source of valuable drugs. In the chapter headed "The Helpful Poisoners" there is a brief account of this genus and its seeds, which have produced valuable heart remedies. Hence to the seekers of starting materials for the making of cortisone *Strophanthus* seemed so promising that intensive search for it was started on a large scale.

With the co-operation of the United States Department of Agriculture, which supplied botanists, an African expedition started in 1949 with the support of two commercial manufacturers and the assistance on technical matters of the New York Botanical Garden. The latter institution collected thousands of seeds and herbarium sheets of *Strophanthus* from all the major botanical gardens in the world, for there was much uncertainty as to which species of *Strophanthus* was the right one and how much seed each vine might yield.

The expedition spent part of 1949 and 1950 in tropical

Africa, well equipped with botanists, organic chemists and other scientists, and soon ran across Father Gerstner, a Catholic priest who knew a lot about *Strophanthus* and had sent many seeds to Switzerland where there was a corps of organic chemists eager to find a precursor of cortisone.

As there are many species of *Strophanthus* in tropical Africa, the expedition spent much frustrating time in collecting seeds from different species, most of which had to be flown to the United States for analysis and which often turned out to be worthless. Another expedition, by the United States Department of Agriculture, was sent to South Africa and the Rhodesias to see if other species of *Strophanthus* might be possible.

The basic trouble with all this work was that the vine produced only moderate amounts of seed, and the collection of these from wild sources proved to be grotesquely inadequate. The seeds are rather small and contain only a fractional amount of the necessary ingredient useful as starting material for the making of cortisone, the demand for which kept on growing. Some idea of the failure of the *Strophanthus* expeditions can be gathered from the fact that only a few hundred pounds of seed ever came from Africa, and the seeds were needed literally in tons.

So acute was this failure that attempts were made to grow the vine in southern Florida and at Mayaquez, Puerto Rico. The plant will grow there satisfactorily, but any attempt to make large-scale plantations of it was punctured by a brilliant organic chemist working in the laboratory of Penn State University.

While *Strophanthus* expeditions were costly failures so far as the commercial manufacture of cortisone is concerned, technically they were far from that. The extraction of cortisone from animal sources involved scouring the slaughterhouses of the world, and even then the conversion of these messy materials, depending on the skill of the chemist, took anywhere from thirty-two to forty distinct steps in order to produce cortisone. But in the case of *Strophanthus* seeds these chemical steps were less than one half those of the animal routine. Such a spectacular reduction in costs pointed the way to what has become a recent and amazing develpment in the production of steroid drugs by an entirely different plant. Cortisone and its derivatives and analogues are still the most important of these steroids and are now produced from this plant on a huge scale.

In the meantime, and in spite of its high initial cost, cortisone had captured the medical world. One development was the production of hydrocortisone, a more effective drug than cortisone and with less undesirable side effects. Many arthritic patients under cortisone complain of "moon face," hirsuteness in females and various psychic and very unpleasant manifestations. Also, if the drug is stopped, they nearly always relapse, sometimes ending up worse than when the drug was started. Also, every doctor knows that under certain conditions some patients should never be given these drugs, notably those having peptic ulcer, tuberculosis, diabetes and several other complaints.

But in spite of these restrictions, cortisone or its derivatives and analogues have taken a place undreamed of thirty years ago. One of them corrects the adrenal insufficiency of Addison's disease. In rheumatic heart disease, bursitis, and dozens of other afflictions these steroid drugs are either life-saving, life-prolonging, or most of all anti-inflammatory, which is why they are so useful in temporary flare-ups of arthritis. Another and very useful attribute of one of these analogues of cortisone is that, applied externally, it is of great value in certain skin diseases. So true is this that one proprietary remedy for this is stated to be responsible for "the greatest percentage of sales of these steroid drugs."—(*Standard and Poor's Report,* June 17, 1964)

Much nonsense was written about this magic "wonder drug." The sober fact is that a tabulation of two recent medical textbooks discloses that these steroid drugs are, or have recently been, used by the profession in over ninety different afflictions. Some of these are serious, such as Addison's disease, asthma (maybe life-saving), gout, hepatitis, leukemia (as palliative), sixteen different eye troubles, pemphigus (often fatal without it), and ulcerative colitis. Either cortisone, corticotropin (ACTH) or hydrocortisone is the mostly likely to be used in these and many other diseases. ACTH (corticotropin) is another important hormone originating in those magical adrenal glands, but is now readily available from manufactured sources.

In spite of the worldwide use of cortisone in so many different diseases, all the experts agree that "Except as replacement therapy in instances of adrenal or pituitary insufficiency, cortisone does not provide a biologic cure for any known disease." But cortisone, hydrocortisone and ACTH provide wonderful correctives for the acute stages of many diseases. Some experts would even deny that these substances are drugs at all, for they certainly differ markedly from such standard drugs as digitalis, morphine or quinine. Upon that theory these steroid hormones are simply manufactured products to replace or improve the natural hormones made in our adrenal glands.

Those who deny that these steroids are drugs in the ordinary sense remind us that these hormones are self-generated products of the adrenal glands, and hence differ fundamentally from drugs that originate elsewhere, such as aspirin, curare, cocaine and scores of others. Some of these hormones of internal secretion dictate important activities of our lives. That they do so in ways that are often somewhat elusive hardly detracts from their imperative usefulness. Among these hormones are those that initiate sex, control the proper balance of critical chemicals in the body, help to regulate blood pressure and often create emotional stresses and anxiety.

Such speculations are best left to the experts, but whether true or false, the use of these steroid hormones has so captured the medical world that a reasonably cheap and abundant source of the starting material became imperative, especially after the failure of the *Strophanthus* expeditions.

The Plant That Won

Of the criteria of accomplishment in science the inclusion of one's name in *American Men of Science* or *Who's Who in America* is usually considered as evidence of superior attainment. But neither of these biographical reference works includes the name of the discoverer of what *Fortune* magazine characterized as "the most remarkable technological contribution ever to come from south of the border." It came from Mexico, but the man responsible for it was an American organic chemist, Russell E. Marker, who was born in Hagerstown, Maryland, in 1902. So outstanding were his accomplishments that one of his highly expert colleagues has characterized them as "the revolutionary nature of Marker's contribution to the steroid industry." (Norman Applezweig in *Steroid Drugs*)

Marker worked for a time at the Rockefeller Institute, then went to Penn State, where he and his associates worked on projects involving plant sterols, financed by one of the leading United States pharmaceutical manufacturers. After publishing one hundred forty-seven papers on these sterols and assigning seventy-five patents to his sponsors, he became convinced that the future of the steroid drugs—cortisone, hydrocortisone, ACTH, and the sex hormones—did not have to rely on animal sources and that certain plants, unlike *Strophanthus*, would supply a cheap and ample source of the starting material for their manufacture.

Technically his conviction was not revolutionary, for the United States Department of Agriculture and many pharmaceutical firms were exploring hundreds of different plants as a possible source of starting materials. Marker's great contribution was to find one that was not only valuable but so plentiful that there would be no question of future supplies. His main choice was a yam—not the "yam" of the shops, which is merely a variety of the sweet potato.

True yams (*Dioscorea*) are vines the swollen roots of which have furnished starchy food to indigent natives throughout the tropics for thousands of years. Some of these edible roots may weigh as much as one hundred pounds, but there is one native in the eastern United States, known as wild yam (*Dioscorea villosa*), which is a scrambling vine with a much smaller root. It was not only these edible yams that interested Marker, for he studied many species of *Dioscorea* from Mexico and the southwestern United States, looking for very different attributes.

Dioscorea has perhaps eighty to ninety different species in Mexico, some of them edible, others used by the natives to stun fish which come to the surface of ponds where the grated roots have been thrown. This is common practice throughout tropical America, where several different plants bring half-stunned fish to the surface—their flesh being safely edible. Marker spent years in Mexico unraveling the complexities of yam botany and chemistry, and even the fish poisons.

His ultimate success has been felt in every pharmaceutical manufacturing firm in the world. What he sought was a species of *Dioscorea*, plentiful enough and easily cultivated, that contained the necessary amount of *sapogenin*, a substance

that practically defies definition, except in the highly technical jargon of the organic chemist. Webster's Dictionary says
it might be "any compound (other than a sugar) obtained by
hydrolysis of a saponin." If that somewhat stuns the layman,
he is no worse off than Mexican fish stunned by *Dioscorea!*

Marker found that the sapogenin-yielding species of Mexican *Dioscorea* were confined to about four or five different
yams. One species, rich in sapogenin, takes twenty years to
produce a mature root. Another, called *barbasco,* matured its
roots in much less time. But barbasco is a baffling term. Every
botanist who has worked in tropical America knows that
there are dozens of different plants with that vernacular name
—all of them fish poisons. Marker finally found what he was
after in a yam (*Dioscorea*) that was very rich in sapogenin,
and matured its roots in only three years. Its particular form
of sapogenin is known today as diosgenin, and because it contained adequate amounts of the starting material for the
manufacture of cortisone and other steroid drugs, it was
hailed as a major discovery. One expert has written that this
Mexican plant "was found just in time, when the demand for
steroids changed from several tons per year to several tons per
month."

The effect upon the European manufacturers of cortisone
and its derivatives was disturbing. The cartel, composed of
several European firms, held by patents and other restrictions
what amounted to a monopoly on the production of steroid
drugs—all derived from the complicated and relatively expensive extraction from animals.

Here, then, was a plant source that seemed adequate,
plentiful and far cheaper. It is a curious reflection on the
American pharmaceutical industry that Marker's offer to find
starting materials from Mexican plants was turned down as
visionary and probably impractical. Today they know better,
and no doubt wish they had the technical skill and imagina-

tion of this organic chemist who broke the bottleneck of steroid production.

This, of course, did not come overnight. Determination of the right species of *Dioscorea* was far from being able to harvest enough roots to be significant. It needed several years and a lot of capital to ensure adequate supplies, and no one knew this better than Marker. Besides being an expert organic chemist, he set about the practical realization of the problem of adequate production.

His solution reads like a fairy tale. In a comparatively primitive laboratory in Mexico City, he produced several kilograms of one of the sex hormones then worth about $80,000 per kilo (2.2 lbs.), so rare and difficult to make was this precious stuff. He worked, ate and slept in his laboratory and was so fearful of someone stealing his secret formula that he carried it with him whenever he left the building. This was not an entirely unnecessary precaution, for the European cartel for the production of hormones was already apprehensive at the possibility that Marker's use of diosgenin from *Dioscorea* might threaten their monopoly.

Marker at this stage of his career determined to cash in on his discovery, which American pharmaceutical firms had dismissed as impractical. He took his precious material to, and ultimately joined forces with, Hormona Laboratories S.A. This Mexican firm was already working on the production of hormones under the direction of men who had formerly been with the Hungarian firm of Gedeon Richter. In 1944, Marker and the owners of Hormona founded the firm of Syntex S.A., a wholly Mexican corporation.

Why Marker left Syntex is the subject of much speculation and a good deal of probably incorrect "explanations." At any rate he went within a year, leaving behind him at least the outline of his precious formulas. Later he organized Hormosynth S.A. in association with the Hungarian firm of Gedeon

Richter. Marker retired from Hormosynth in 1952, which then took the name of Diosynth S.A.

In the meantime Syntex began a large-scale cultivation and collection of *Dioscorea,* mostly in southern Mexico. So extensive was this that they ultimately comprised products from thousands of wild and cultivated acres and produced diosgenin on such a scale that one of the hormones that cost $80 per gram when they started was selling at less than $2 per gram ten years later. Some idea of the size of these operations can be gleaned from the fact that in a single year *Dioscorea* was harvested to the extent of over sixty thousand tons of fresh root. Such a huge production was necessary because of the ever-increasing demand for steroid drugs, and *Dioscorea* was obviously becoming the chief source for the starting material in their manufacture. It is little wonder that Dr. Norman Applezweig, one of Marker's associates, has been quoted as estimating that from 70 to 75 per cent of the starting materials for the manufacture of hormones now comes from the diosgenin in *Dioscorea.*

Perhaps no plant product in the history of medicine has had such a spectacular career. Its value is probably ten times that of the Dutch cartel on quinine. One estimate states that $30 million per year is the cost of the crude *Dioscorea* roots from which finished products worth $100 million are extracted annually. In the drug field that is big business, and it is little wonder that a group of Americans bought control of Syntex S.A. from its Mexican owners.

While its roots are still in Mexico, Syntex moved its research staff and laboratories to Palo Alto, California, in 1960. There, under the name of Syntex Laboratories, Inc., they maintain a highly trained corps of experts and, according to several appraisals, have become "one of the largest steroid chemical research organizations in the world." Also they are headquarters for the supply of the starting materials that are ordered by nearly all the pharmaceutical manufacturers. Almost one quarter of the stock of Syntex is owned by a single Wall Street firm.

The impact of the *Dioscorea* miracle was acutely felt, especially in tropical America. Scheering, a large German chemical firm, started a yam plantation in Guatemala, and two or three competitors of Syntex in Mexico were also active. But none of these is comparable to Syntex. Also the availability of diosgenin from Mexico affected every hormone manufacturer in the world, especially those members of the European cartel, most of whom, with a few American firms, were still relying on the extractives from animals.

This triumph of *Dioscorea* also set off a relatively frantic struggle between rival American firms, based on the difficulty and cost of converting diosgenin into finished hormones. Some of these processes are secret, others are amply protected by patents, and a somewhat bewildering system of licensing arrangements has been worked out. These details are no doubt of paramount importance to the firms involved, but the net result to the public is an ample supply of these drugs at a fraction of their cost twenty years ago.

It was Marker's original contention that *Dioscorea* was by no means the only practical source of a sapogenin. He announced that several plants in closely related families might also be useful. These and hundreds of others have since been analyzed for their sapogenin content, and all but three or four are now of interest only to a handful of experts. The search, however, is still very active, for no one knows when *Dioscorea* may be supplanted by a higher-yielding and still cheaper plant. The rewards are so great that botanists and organic chemists are unlikely to abandon the search.

Two of Marker's plants containing sapogenin are members of the same group as the common century plant. All of its three hundred species are tropical American, belonging to the genus *Agave,* and among them are sisal and henequen, both fiber plants. Sisal (*Agave sisalina*) is now cultivated on a large scale in South Africa and in Java. In the extraction of the fiber there is a tremendous residue of sap and the remains of its very fleshy leaves, both of which yield appreciable amounts of sapogenin.

In Yucatán another species of *Agave,* the henequen (*Agave fourcroydes*), with much longer leaves than sisal, yields a valuable fiber, the extraction of which leaves behind a huge amount of what the natives call bagasse. This sap-soaked fleshy material also contains sapogenin, but these practically waste materials of sisal and henequen are not likely to supplant *Dioscorea* just yet, although both yield an appreciable amount of sapogenin.

Two other plants also contain this starting material, one of which is a *Yucca,* related to the common Spanish bayonet of the southeastern United States. The other is the oil pressed out of the seeds of the soybean. As yet, neither of these is much of a threat to the Mexican yam.

But so avid are the chemists to find sapogenin-yielding plants that a learned trio of them pointed to the Joshua tree (*Yucca brevifolia*) of the southwestern United States. The first white man to see this bizarre bit of desert vegetation was Captain John C. Frémont, who called it "the most repulsive tree in the vegetable kingdom." The trees look so grotesquely unreal and are so unique that the United States government set up an area of 1,344 square miles as the Joshua-tree National Monument, about one hundred miles east of San Bernardino, California. The tree is never likely to supplant *Dioscorea.*

Another, and perhaps still more important, aftermath of the development of the Mexican yam industry was the vast increase in knowledge of the organic chemists and endocrinologists. Until a few years ago, hormones were well known to be highly important. But the chemical composition of these highly elusive pyxies was rather fragmentary and the mechanism of their action still a bit mysterious. In fact, one expert in the field has intimated that steroid drugs and the natural hormones are about as difficult chemically as anything else in that science.

In spite of these difficulties, the chemists have produced dozens of steroid drugs, some from the diosgenin of *Dioscorea*, but others practically tailor-made in the laboratory. For the layman perhaps the simplest classification of these complexities is to record their three most important divisions. All are hormones, some of them purely synthetic, but most of them using the Mexican yam as starting material.

1. Hormones of the adrenal cortex. These include cortisone and its derivatives and analogues, used mostly as clinical drugs for specific diseases such as rheumatoid arthritis and any other afflictions.

2. Female sex hormones, notably estrone and progesterone. They are widely used in correcting deficiencies or augmenting the natural functions of female reproductive organs.

3. Male sex hormones, of which the best known is testosterone, although there are several others. These have been used in cases of male deficiencies; psychiatric difficulties and, in reduced dosage, for correction of hormonal imbalance in females.

In *Chemical Week* for April 4, 1964, there is a hint that in spite of these technical and industrial triumphs, there had been a disturbing lull in the sale of steroid drugs. Perhaps it was not surprising, considering that the most important of them, cortisone, was no real cure for rheumatoid arthritis or for any other disease. Little did the public or the industry know that, just around the corner, was a discovery that exploded with more violence than anything else in the fantastic history of steroid drugs. Its effect was startling on several fronts, notably among women, the clergy, the medical profession and upon the floor of the American Stock Exchange.

Babies by Choice or by Chance

Such is the provocative title of an absorbing book by Dr. A. F. Guttmacher, issued in 1959. The conception of unwanted babies is so huge that in Japan, where abortion is legal and almost universally safe, abortions exceed the number of births. For thousands of years women have schemed to prevent conception and, failing it, have resorted to often dangerous and sometimes fatal abortions, which are illegal in the United States except where medical opinion considers them imperative.

Even as early as 338 B.C., Aristotle tells us that some Greek women tried to prevent conception by "anointing that part of the womb upon which the seed will fall, with oil of cedar or ointment of lead or frankincense commingled with olive oil." Ever since then various nostrums, jellies, diaphragms and other devices have been used, not one of which is one hundred per cent effective, while some of them are esthetically repulsive.

The Roman Catholic Church cannot be naïve enough to think they originated the so-called rhythm method, for it is nothing new. Hindu medical schools, around 500 B.C., were advocating that "impregnation is impossible during about twelve days of the menstrual cycle." Biologically this may be nearly correct, but restraint is easier to advocate than to observe.

The truth of this age-old problem is that none of these methods is certain, and until 1958 there was no regime, except abstinence, that would guarantee the prevention of conception. But abstinence is a rather chilly doctrine, slightly more popular with the clergy of the Roman Catholic Church than with their parishioners or the rest of us. All these uncertainties were quite recently settled in a laboratory at Worcester, Massachusetts.

While the not unpopular mechanics of human conception have been known for thousands of years, the process and its results contained many hidden secrets, most of them involving the sex hormones. And while it is still true that population growth generally depends upon erotic drive, not until the 1930's was there scientific proof that these sex hormones both sparked that drive and were essential to any successful pregnancy that might result from it.

One of the most significant by-products of the study of these steroid drugs was a wealth of information about the importance of hormones in pregnancy. The experts have unraveled a huge amount of data on the chemistry of these sex hormones and even designed drugs to aid pregnancy, prevent habitual abortion, help infertility, correct some "female complaints," but most of all, and most controversially, to prevent conception without resort to abstinence.

Not all of this work was done at the Worcester Foundation for Experimental Biology, but in 1956 Dr. Gregory Pincus and his team at that institution shot a thunderbolt. They announced that one of the drugs derived indirectly from Mexican *Dioscorea* would stop ovulation and hence prevent conception. There were already several steroid drugs that prevent conception, but all of them up to that time had to be given by injection, a domestically impossible handicap. But Pincus had a compound called 19-norprogesterone, mercifully abbreviated to 19-nor, a drug that could be taken by mouth.

Two fairly large-scale tests of the new drug were started in the Puerto Rico Family Planning Center and at the Los Angeles Planned Parenthood Center. Conception did not occur in any of these normally fertile wives, so long as they meticulously followed the doctor's directions of taking one pill a day from the fifth to the twenty-fifth day of the normal twenty-eight-day menstrual cycle. Even in those who forgot to take the pill for a few days, pregnancy resulted in only a few cases.

That 19-nor could accomplish such a feat as preventing ovulation seemed then almost miraculous. The extraordinarily complex interaction of the female sex hormones normally results in the descent of the ovules only during a specified time, when their impregnation by motile spermatozoa is at least possible and may be certain. But 19-nor, and some recent improvements of it, completely stops the descent of the ovules and makes pregnancy impossible, while allowing nearly normal completion of the cycle ending in the monthly menstruation.

Another remarkable attribute of 19-nor and its successors is that women who stop the regime can later have normal pregnancies and give birth to normal babies. Taken under the direction of a physician, and it should be taken no other way, it is apparently a safe medication and the United States Pure Food and Drug Administration has given its approval of it. The drug has a few undesirable side effects, but not enough to warrant its discontinuance. But it should not be forgotten, however, that its use is interfering chemically with the delicately balanced hormonal functions of the reproductive system and hence needs medical supervision.

So far there has been little or no evidence that long-time use of this anti-fertility pill has any permanent deleterious effects. There are physicians who wonder whether chemical interference with pregnancy may breed latent troubles in the future. But except for the contraindications to the use of any steroid drug, there is little support for such fears. It is true, however, that its use is comparatively recent.

Soon after the completion of the successful tests in Puerto

Rico and Los Angeles, practically every pharmaceutical manufacturer in the world was making his own brand of the drug
under varying trade names, and today millions of women are
steady users of them. It costs them about $2.50 to $3.00 per
month in the United States, but considerably less than this in
England and on the continent.

The basic material for these new drugs is generally the
diosgenin from Mexican *Dioscorea,* and the chief supplier of
this is still Syntex. While a few of these steroid drugs are
wholly synthetic, the great bulk of them use diosgenin as the
starting material for their manufacture. The effect upon the
profits of Syntex was so great that a fever of speculation ensued on the Stock Exchange. Stock of Syntex that cost $66 per
share in October, 1963, jumped to $190, only to fall back to
$89. Such wild fluctuations prompted investigation by the
Securities and Exchange Commission and by the American
Stock Exchange. The stock of another American firm, involved in a big way with the new anti-fertility pill, also went
from $62 to $85 within a fortnight.

In June, 1964, the president of Syntex stated that the sale
of this contraceptive pill "would reach $40,000,000 at the
manufacturer's level," and another American firm has applied to the government of India for permission to build a
factory there, where the need for population control is acute.
So conscious of this is India that the government opened
eight thousand family planning centers in 1963.

Perhaps no other drug in such a short time has had such a
worldwide use. It has the disadvantage that it must be taken
under medical supervision, is relatively costly for indigent
people and must be taken every day for twenty days. In
affluent America the cost is not much more than that of a
couple of good movies. But in India, Indonesia, Malaya,
South America and parts of Africa, its cost is prohibitive and

their governments are already talking of free or nearly free distribution.

The anti-fertility pill has been of incalculable value to the families that use it. Reasonably affluent ones often question whether the addition of one or two more babies will not curtail the educational future of the whole brood. Now they can space them to ease the mother's burdens, or stop having any more for the benefit of those clamoring for higher education. Also the pill has desirable esthetic and emotional effects, for many frigid women blame their frigidity on the fear of pregnancy.

If the impact of the pill caused flurries on the Stock Exchange and an avalanche of gratitude from its users, its impact on the Roman Catholic Church was little less than an uproar. The Church has traditionally advocated abstinence, which is difficult, or the rhythm method, which is grudgingly followed and only partly effective. But here the Church was faced with a new and amazing scientific technique. What could they do about a drug that produced no abortions and avoided conception by the apparently simple device of preventing the ovules from ever getting where that is possible?

The first gun was fired by Pope Pius XII, a month before he died. He said that the pill, while useful under the doctor's supervision to treat "reproductive disorders," was "morally unacceptable as a form of sterilization." The pill, like all other forms of contraception, "violates natural and divine law."

His successor, Pope John XXIII, appeared to be a little less drastic in his adherence to traditional Catholic doctrine. He well knew that one of his dreams was some form of rapprochement between Catholic and Protestant communicants, but it was crystal-clear that no Protestant Church would ban the pill or any other form of contraception. That impasse was far from settled at any of the Ecumenical Councils, up to the third.

As late as June 23, 1964, Pope Paul VI said that "up to now we do not have sufficient motive to consider out of date, and therefore not binding, the norms given by Pope Pius XII in this regard. Therefore, they must be considered valid, at least until we feel obliged in conscience to change them."

That regression to traditional Catholic doctrine has met with a very varied response. Recent surveys of Catholic families reveal that perhaps 70 per cent of them practice some sort of contraception, including the pill. One mother of four children in New Jersey stated that she takes the pill but does not confess it "because I don't consider it a sin." Perhaps the most impressive advocate of the pill is a distinguished Roman Catholic gynecologist, Dr. John Rock, who collaborated with Dr. Pincus in the work that sparked the pill. Dr. Rock, for years on the staff of the Harvard Medical School, sees no problem in the use of the pill by Roman Catholics. He has been a devout member of that church for many years and was married by the late Cardinal O'Connell of Boston.

Such distinguished sponsorship of the oral contraceptive pill has not gone unnoticed by the Church. Msgr. George A. Kelly, director of the Family Life Bureau of the Archdiocese of New York, has stated that "The sex organs were made by God to reproduce the human race." And, again, "People can live a life of continence in marriage. But now they are being told they can use the pill and have more fun." Another argument against the pill is its use on college campuses, where a girl will tell a boy, falsely, that she is using the pill and may precipitate him into unwanted fatherhood.

Perhaps the most searing of ecclesiastical strictures against Dr. Rock came from Msgr. Francis W. Carney of Cleveland, who called the dedicated physician a "moral rapist." What causes such divergent views, and has split part of the Church so fundamentally, is that for the first time in a thousand years the Church may have to listen to its parishioners instead of dictating to them. Such a concept raises all sorts of questions that have nothing to do with a pill derived from a Mexican *Dioscorea*. But it is undeniable that the yam has touched off a controversy that has shaken the Church.

And an even more controversial issue is just around the corner. One great objection to the present anti-fertility pill is the fact that it must be taken for twenty days and costs too much for indigent people who need it the most. The organic chemists working on the sex hormones may soon announce the safety, simplicity and effectiveness of a new pill designed for a very different purpose. The present pill prevents ovulation, but the new one will permit that perfectly normal incident of the monthly menstrual cycle. If, however, there is a union of the microscopic spermatozoa and the equally microscopic egg cell (ovum), fertilization will have taken place, and left to itself the egg cell will inevitably lead to pregnancy.

At this particular juncture the new pill biologically suppresses or stifles the fertilized egg cell long before it will have time to develop into a viable, extremely minute and rudimentary embryo, and weeks before it becomes a fetus. Such a dramatic interference with pregnancy may require only one pill a month, and some scientists are already hinting that a single pill per year may ensure freedom from pregnancy.

This pill is not yet on the market, but it opens up vistas for the freedom of mankind to decide for themselves whether babies are to come by chance or by choice. That it is even more controversial than the present pill is obvious. While the Church may ultimately have to condone the present pill, there is little doubt that the stifling or suppression of a fertilized ovum, however microscopic, will be bitterly opposed, not only by the Church but by some others.

The answer of the scientists who are working on the new

pill is a drastic denial of religious or legal restraints to its use. They point out that there is little difference to them between the use of sex hormones to control habitual abortion, and to help in the problems of infertility, in both of which they have wide and valued use, and their ability to control pregnancy. They look on all these functions as biological rather than moral problems, the choice of which should be left to them, without interference from any church. If present laws conflict, they believe they should be changed.

They further argue, with considerable cogency, that since modern science has uncovered a wealth of information on the unsuspected importance of the sex hormone, why deny us the benefits of it? Why not control the hitherto uncontrollable results of sexual intercourse? As one of the scientists puts it, "If man now uses hormones to free childbearing from its primary dependence upon erotic drive, he will really be using his brain."

If this book was a biography of scientists instead of a record of their exploits, it would contain the lives of a galaxy of the great. For our survival in a hostile world, well supplied with destructive diseases, is largely due to the men who explored the plant world for the remedies for them.

In heart disease it was the Birmingham physician, Dr. William Withering. For malaria the saintly Cardinal de Lugo, followed by the fabulous quack Robert Talbor, the dedicated French chemists Pelletier and Caventou, and finally Sir Ronald Ross, all of whom contributed to the fantastic quinine story. Among the greatest of all was Sertürner, an obscure German chemist, who not only discovered morphine, but first explained the nature of a plant alkaloid.

The almost mythical emperor of China, Shen Nung, was writing about rhubarb and ephedra five thousand years before Dr. Chen told the Western world about it, and long before it acquired the name Mormon tea. And Avicenna, that prince of rakes, was writing about medicinal plants in books that were used by physicians for six hundred years after he died.

Even from central Africa Dr. David Livingstone and another missionary, Dr. Daniell, first told us of dangerous arrow poisons that are now standard remedies. And in Dr. Sigmund Freud's laboratory, a young scientist, Dr. Carl Koller, not yet twenty-three years old, first used cocaine in eye operations. In Burma and southeast Asia Joseph Rock unraveled the mystery of chaulmoogra, then widely used in leprosy. And the immortal Dioscorides, two thousand years ago, first pointed to the tree that steered German chemists to the secret of aspirin.

The list could be extended almost indefinitely, not forgetting Drs. Marker, Kendall and Pincus, who were intimately concerned with the very modern concept of the place hormones occupy in our daily lives. Some of these discoveries are mere whispers from the jungle earth, like curare. But others are the result of highly sophisticated laboratory techniques. Nearly all of these drugs were derived from that vastly opulent plant world that tenaciously holds its secrets, waiting for genius to uncover them.

How the scientists did so and what came of it is thus a history not only of nature's opulence, but of the men who unlocked her secrets—chemists, botanists, pharmacologists and physicians. A devoted band and perhaps more so than most of us, they listened to Dr. William Withering, who wrote:

It is much easier to write upon a disease than upon a remedy. The former is in the hands of nature and a faithful observer with an eye of tolerable judgment cannot fail to delineate a likeness. The latter will ever be subject to the whims, the inaccuracies and the blunders of mankind.

Bibliography

The botanical, medical, pharmacological and athropological literature pertaining to this book is so huge that only a drastic winnowing of it is included. The restricted list of books may guide the seeker to wider fields than are possible here.

Abrams, L. Illustrated flora of the Pacific states (4 volumes). Stanford, California. 1940-1960.

Ackerknecht, E. H. Primitive medicine and culture patterns. *Bull. of the History of Med.*, 12:545-574. Baltimore. 1942.

Applezweig, Norman. Steroid drugs (pp. 1-742). New York. 1962.

Arny, L. W. Breeding for atropine. *Journ. Heredity*, 8:164-167. 1917.

Baer, K. A., and Spencer, M. The pituitary-adrenocortical functions: ACTH, cortisone and related compounds. Army Med. Library (pp. 1-366). Washington. 1950.

Barber, G. W., Peterson, D. H., and Ehrenstein, M. Investigations on steroids. XXXI. Preparation of 19-Hydroxycorticosterone. *Journ. Organic Chem.*, 25:1168-1174. 1960.

Barnard, C. The Duboisias of Australia. *Economic Botany*, 6:3-17. 1952.

Baron, Richard. The flora of Madagascar. *Journ. Linn. Soc. Botany*, 25:246-294. 1884.

Barton, N., et al. Studies on the chemical constitution of colchicine. *Chem. & Ind.*, 1945:103. 1945.

Bernhard-Smith, A. Poisonous plants of all countries (pp. 1-112). London. 1923.

Birth Control: The pill and the Church. *Newsweek*. July 6, 1964.

Blubaugh, L. V., and Linegar, C. R. Curare and modern medicine. *Economic Botany*, 2:73-82. 1948.

Boland, E. W., and Headley, N. E. Effects of cortisone acetate on rheumatoid arthritis. *Journ. Am. Med. Assoc.*, 141:301-308. 1949.

Bonisteel, W. J. Atropa Belladonna *Addisonia*. 16: plate 527. 1931.

Bovet, D., Bovet-Nitti, F., and Marini-Bettolo, G. B. Curare and curare-like agents (pp. 1-478). Amsterdam. 1959.

Boyd, M. F. An introduction to malariology (pp. 1-437). Cambridge. 1930.

Brewer, W. R., and Laurie, A. Culture studies of the drug plant Atropa belladonna. *Ohio Agri. Exp. Sta. Bimo. Bull.*, 29:159-167. 1944.

Cavane, P. A dissertation on oleum Palmae Christi or Castor Oil (pp. 1-33). Bath, England. No date but surely before 1750.

Chaudri, I. I. Pakistani Ephedra. *Economic Botany*, 11: 257-262. 1957.

Chen, K. K., and Kao, C. H. Ephedrine and pseudoephedrine. *Journ. Am. Pharm. Assoc.*, 15:625-639. 1926.

Chen, K. K., and Ling, A. S. H. Fragments of Chinese medical history (pp. 1-6). New York. 1926.

Chen, K. K., and Schmidt, C. F. The action of ephedrine, the active principle of the Chinese drug mahuang. *Journ. Pharm. & Exp. Therapeutics*, 24:339-357. 1924.

—— The action and clinical use of ephedrine. *Journ. Am. Med. Assoc.*, 87:836-842. 1926.

—— Ephedrine and related substances (pp. 1-121). Baltimore. 1930.

Cheney, R. H. The ancient and modern use of plant arrow poisons. *Scientific Monthly*, 23:552-555. 1926.

—— Geographic and taxonomic distribution of American plant arrow poisons. *Am. Journ. Bot.*, 18:136-145. 1931.

Chin, T. C., and Youngken, H. W. The cytotaxonomy of Rheum. *Am. Journ. Bot.*, 34:401-407. 1947.

Chock, A. K. Joseph F. Rock, 1884-1962. *Am. Hort. Mag.*, 42:158-167. 1963.

Chopra, R. H. Hypnotic effect of *Rauwolfia serpentina:* The principle underlying its actions: its probable nature. *Ind. Journ. Med. Research*, 31:71-74. 1943.

Christensen, B. V., and Hiner, L. D. Cultivation of *Ephedra sinica* in South Dakota. *Journ. Am. Pharm. Assoc.*, 28:199-209. 1939.

Clendening, Logan. Source book of medical history (pp. 1-685). New York. 1942.

Collis, Maurice. Foreign mud: The opium imbroglio at Canton (pp. 1-300). New York. 1947.

Cooper, S. A dissertation on the properties and effects of the Datura Stramonium (pp. 1-58). Philadelphia. 1797.

Cornatzer, W. E., McEwen, M. M., and Andrews, J. C. Schizonticidal tests on Rauwolfia heterophylla and some other proposed anti-malarial plants. *Journ. Elisha Mitchell Sci. Soc.*, 60:167-170. 1944.

Correll, D. C., Schubert, B. G., Gentry, H. S., and Hawley, W. O. The search for plant precursors of cortisone. *Economic Botany*, 9:307-375. 1955.

Coutela, J. G. Historie, botanique, chimeque, commerciale et pharma-cologique de la rhubarbe (pp. 1-56). Paris. 1869.

Deger, Erwin. La verdad acerca de la Chalchupa (pp. 1-4). Guatemala. 1938.

Desfontaines, R. L. Memoire sur le jalap. *Ann. du Museum. 2. Nat. Hist.* pp. 120-130. Paris. 1813.

Dioscorides. *See* GUNTHER.

Doebel, K., Schlittler, E., and Reichstein, T. Beitrag zur Kenntnis des Antiarins. *Helvetica Chim. Acta*, 31:688-709. 1948.

Domingo, W. E. The development of domestic castor bean production. *Economic Botany*, 7:65-75. 1953.

Dorland, W. A. N. American illustrated medical dictionary (pp. 1-1660). 21st Edition. Philadelphia. 1947.

Duran-Reynals, M. L. The fever bark tree (pp. 1-275). New York. 1946.

Dutcher, J. D. Curare alkaloids from Chondodendron tomentosum. *Journ. Am. Chem. Soc.*, 68:419-424. 1946.

Dutta, P. K., Chopra, I. C. and Kapoor, L. D. Cultivation of *Rauwolfia serpentina* in India. *Economic Botany*, 17:243-251. 1963.

Dyer, W. T. T. Ipoh poison of the peninsula. Kew *Bulletin Misc. Information*, No. 50., pp. 25-31. 1891.

Ellenhorn, M. J. The F D A and the prevention of drug embryopathy. *Bull. N.Y. Acad. Med.*, 40:661-673. 1964.

Fantus, B. Useful cathartics: the use and abuse of cathartics (pp. 1-120). Chicago. 1920.

Folkers, K. Preliminary studies of the botanical components of Tecuna and Java curare. *Journ. Am. Pharm. Assoc.*, 27:689-693. 1938.

Forsdike, J. L., and Meek, H. O. Indian squill and its differentiation from European squill. *Pharmaceut. Journ.*, 157:104. 1946.

Forsham, P. H. Present status of ACTH and Cortisone in therapy. *Med. Clinics N. Am.*, 1951:1229-1253. 1951.

Fraser, T. R. The characters, actions and therapeutic uses of the Ordeal Bean of Calabar (pp. 1-44). Edinburgh. 1863.

—— *Strophanthus hispidus,* its natural history, chemistry and pharmacology (pp. 1-190). Edinburgh. 1891.

Frazer, J. G. The native races of Africa and Madagascar (pp. 1-578). London, 1938.

—— The golden bough (pp. 1-752). New York. 1945.

Gerlach, G. H. *Datura innoxia:* a potential commercial source of scopolamine. *Economic Botany,* 2:436-454. 1948.

Gerste, A. Notes sur la medicine et la botanique des anciens Mexicains (pp. 1-161). Rome. 1909.

Gold, Harry. Quinidine in disorders of the heart (pp. 1-115). New York. 1950.

—— Experiences in human pharmacology. In *Quantitative Methods in Human Pharmacology* (pp. 40-54). New York. 1959.

Goodman, Louis, and Gilman, Alfred. The pharmacological basis of therapeutics (pp. 1-1383). New York. 1941.

Gorkom, K. W. van. A handbook of cinchona culture (pp. 1-292). Amsterdam. 1883.

Groff, G. W., and Clark, G. W. The botany of Ephedra in relation to the yield of physiologically active substances. *Univ. of Calif. Pubs. Botany,* 14:247-282. 1928.

Gunther, R. T. The Greek herbal of Dioscorides (pp. 1-701). Oxford. 1934.

Gupta, J. C., Kahali, B. S., and Dutta, A. T. The hypnotic effect of a resin isolated from the root of Rauwolfia serpentina. *Indian Journ. Med. Research,* 32:183-188. 1944.

Gutierrez-Noriega, C., and Ortiz, V. Z. Estudios sobre la Coca y la Cocaina en el Peru (pp. 1-134). Lima. 1947.

Gutierrez-Noriega, C., and von Hagen, V. W. Coca: The mainstay of an arduous native life in the Andes. *Economic Botany,* 5:145-152. 1951.

Guttmacher, A. F. Babies by choice or by chance (pp. 1-289). 1959.

Hackett, L. W. Malaria in Europe (pp. 1-336). London. 1937.

Haggis, A. W. Fundamental errors in the early history of *Cinchona. Bull. of the History of Med.,* 10:417-459 + 568-592. Baltimore. 1941.

Hamied, Y. K. Diosgenin and the steroid hormones. *The Pharmaceutist,* March, 1962: 43-44. 1962.

Hanslik, P. J. 125th Anniversary of the discovery of Morphine by Sertürner. *Journ. Am. Pharm. Assoc.,* 18:375-385. 1929.

Harley, John. The old vegetable neurotics: opium, belladonna and henbane (pp. 1-355). London. 1869.

Hassal, C. H. Alkaloidal constituents of New Zealand ergot. *N. Z. Journ. Sci. and Tech.,* 25B:169-174. 1944.

Henry, T. A. The plant alkaloids (pp. 1-689). Philadelphia. 1939.

Hill, A. W. The genus *Strychnos* in India and the East. Kew *Bull. Misc. Information,* 1917:122-210. 1917.

Hills, K. L. Duboisia in Australia. *Journ. N.Y. Bot. Gard.*, 49:185-188. 1948.

Hills, K. L., and Kelenyi, G. P. Preliminary report upon the cultivation of Duboisia spp. Australian Council *Sci. & Indust. Res. Journ.*, 19:359-375. 1946.

Himwich, H. E. Tranquilizing drugs (pp. 1-197). Washington. 1957.

Hocking, G. M. Indian rhubarb. *Indian Journ. Pharmacy*, 7:89-92. 1945.

—— Henbane: healing herb of Hercules and of Apollo. *Economic Botany*, 1:306-316. 1947.

Hodge, W. H. The drug aloes of commerce with special reference to the Cape species. *Economic Botany*, 7:99-129. 1953.

Hosseus, C. C. Rhizome Rhei. *Revista del Centro Estudiantes de Farmacia*, 1:57-69. Cordoba. 1925.

Hughes, J. D., and Clark, J. A., Jr. Stramonium poisoning. *Journ. Am. Med. Assoc.*, 112:2500-2502. 1939.

Ingle, D. J., and Baker, B. L. Physiological and therapeutic effects of corticotropin (ACTH) and cortisone (pp. 1-172). Springfield, Ill. 1953.

Jacobs, W. A., and Craig, L. C. The alkaloids of Veratrum viride. *Journ. Biol. Chem.*, 160:555-565. 1945.

Johnson, D. McL. The hallucinogenic drugs: the insanity producing drugs, Indian hemp and Datura (pp. 1-45). London. 1953.

Johnston, H. H. British Central Africa (pp. 1-471). London. 1897.

Keller, C. Madagascar, Mauritius and other East African islands (pp. 1-242). London. 1901.

Keys to the International Hormone Hassle. *Chem. Week*, July 14, 1956:20-21. 1956.

Kirsch, Bruno. Strophanthin: clinical and experimental experiences of the past 25 years (pp. 1-158). Brooklyn. 1944.

Komroff, M. The travels of Marco Polo (pp. 1-370). New York. 1930.

Kreig, M. B. Green medicine (pp. 1-462). New York. 1964.

Krukoff, B. A., and Moldenke, H. N. Studies of American Menispermaceae, with special reference to species used in preparation of arrow poisons. *Brittonia*, 3:1-74. 1938.

Krukoff, B. A., and Smith, A. C. Notes on the botanical components of curare. *Bull. Torrey Bot. Club*, 64:401-409. 1937.

Langer, Elinor. Drug safety. *Science*, 18 September, 1964 (pp. 1284-1288). 1964.

Lasagna, L. Problems of drug development. *Science*, 145:362-367. 1964.

Lennox, W. G. Ergonovine versus ergotamine as terminator of migraine headaches. *Am. Jour. Med. Sci.*, 195:458-468. 1938.

Lennox, W. G., and Storch, T. J. C. von. Experience with ergotamine tartrate in 120 patients with migraine. *Jour. Am. Med. Assoc.*, 105:169-171. 1935.

Liddell, R. W. Study of the chemistry of cascara sagrada. *Bull. Pittsburgh Univ.*, 37:176-179. 1941.

Lilly, Eli & Co. Monograph on ephedrine (pp. 1-75). Indianapolis. 1941.

Lloyd, J. U. Origin and history of all the pharmacopoeial vegetable drugs (pp. 1-449). Cincinnati. 1929.

Losina-Losinskaya, A. S. The genus Rheum. *Acta. Instit. Bot. Acad. Sci.,* Series 1, Fasc. 3. Moscow. 1936. (English summary.)

Macht, D. I. The holy incense (pp. 1-81). Baltimore. 1928.

Making New Stir in Steroid Markets. *Chemical Week,* April 4, 1964 (pp. 21-23). 1964.

Mariani, Angelo. Coca and its therapeutic application (pp. 1-78). New York. 1896.

Marker, R. E., *et al.* Steroidal sapogenins. *Journ. Am. Chem. Soc.,* 69:2167. 1947.

Markham, C. R. Peruvian bark (pp. 1-550). London. 1880.

Martin, H. E., and Weiss, Soma. The use of physostigmin in abdominal distention. *Journ. Am. Med. Assoc.,* 84:1407-1408. 1925.

Martinez, M. Plantas utiles de Mexico (pp. 1-414). Mexico. 1936.

May, J. M. Siam doctor (pp. 1-255). New York. 1949.

McIntyre, A. R. Curare—Its history, nature and clinical use (pp. 1-240). Chicago. 1947.

Means, P. A. Ancient civilizations of the Andes (pp. 1-586). New York. 1942.

Mellan, I., and Mellan, E. Dictionary of poisons (pp. 1-150). New York. 1956.

Merck & Co. Cortone: A handbook of therapy (pp. 1-129). Rahway, N.J. 1952. (A trade name for cortisone.)

Merck Manual. Tenth Edition (pp. 1-1907). Rahway, N.J. 1961.

Miller, T. G. Clinical value of ephedrine, with report on its effects in certain special cases. *Am. Journ. Med. Sci.,* 170:157-181. 1925.

Missouri Botanical Garden. Proceedings of the celebration of the three hundredth anniversary of the first recognized use of Cinchona (pp. 1-258). St. Louis. 1931.

Moldenke, H. N., and Moldenke, A. L. Plants of the Bible (pp. 1-328). Waltham, Mass. 1952.

Monachino, Joseph. Strophanthus, sarmentogenin and cortisone. The botanical aspects of the story of the newest "Miracle Drug." *Journ. N.Y. Bot. Gard.,* 51:25-39. 1950.

—— Recent developments in Strophanthus as a precursor of Cortisone. *Journ. N.Y. Bot. Gard.,* 51:233-241. 1950.

—— Strophanthus glabriflorus., *Bull. Torrey Bot. Club,* 80:412-414. 1953.

—— *Rauvolfia serpentina:* Its history, botany and medical use. *Economic Botany,* 8:349-365. 1954.

—— Chinese herbal medicine. *Economic Botany,* 10:42-48. 1956.

—— A sarmentogeniferous variety of Strophanthus sarmentosus. *Bull. Torrey Bot. Club,* 83:281-288. 1956.

Monroe, E. W., Warnock, B. H., and Willaman, J. J. Steroidal sapogenins: their occurrence in *Agave Lecheguilla. Economic Botany,* 16:266-269. 1962.

Mortimer, W. G. Peru: History of Coca (pp. 1-576). New York. 1901.

Morton, J. F. Folk uses and commercial exploitation of *Aloe* leaf pulp. *Economic Botany,* 15:311-319. 1961.

Moulton, C. W. A biographical encyclopedia of medical history (pp. 1-367). New York, 1905.

Nelson, A. Medical botany (pp. 1-544). Edinburgh. 1951.

Ogot, B. From Chief to President. *Atlas,* 7:24-28. 1964.

Osborn, C. S. Madagascar: Land of the man-eating tree (pp. 1-443). New York. 1924.

Osol, A., and Farrar, G. E. The dispensatory of the United States of America (pp. 1-2379). Philadelphia. 1960.

Peck, T. W., and Wilkinson, K. D. William Withering of Birmingham (pp. 1-239). Bristol. 1950.

Pelletier, J., and Caventou, J. Analyse chimique des Quinquina (pp. 1-88). Paris. 1821.

S. B. Penick & Co. Rauwolfia and its alkaloids (pp. 1-50). New York. 1956.

Chas. Pfizer & Co. Rauwolfia and derivatives: an annotated bibliography (pp. 1-59). Brooklyn. 1956.

Prasad, S. The influence of fertilizers on the growth and alkaloidal content of Hyoscyamus niger. *Journ. Am. Pharm. Assoc.,* 35:121-127. 1946.

Qazilbash, N. A. Some observations on Indian Artemisias. *Quart. Journ. Pharm. & Pharmacol.,* 15:323-331. 1942.

Raffauf, R. F., and Flagler, M. B. Alkaloids of the Apocynaceae. *Economic Botany,* 14:37-55. 1961.

Ray, John. A collection of curious travels and voyages, in two volumes. Vol. 1. Dr. Leonhart Rauwolf's travels into the eastern countries (pp. 1-396). London. 1693.

Read, B. E. Ephedra, Part II. The botany of mahuang (pp. 1-28). Peiping. 1930.

—— Chinese medicinal plants (pp. 1-389). Peking. 1936.

Reichinger, K. H. Ephedraceae: In Flora Iranica, the flora of Iranian highlands, Afghanistan, West Pakistan, northern Iraq and Turkestan (pp. 1-8). Graz, Austria. 1963.

Reserpine and other alkaloids of *Rauwolfia serpentina.* Symposium. *Ann. N.Y. Acad. Sci.,* 59:1-140. 1954.

Rhind, William. A history of the vegetable kingdom (pp. 1-744). London. 1877.

Riedl, H. Ephedraceae. In *Symbolae Afghanicae.* V (pp. 1-13). Copenhagen. 1963.

Robertson, D. A. On the Calabar Bean as a new agent in ophthalmic medicine. *Medical Classics,* 1:877-885. 1937.

Roddis, L. H. William Withering (pp. 1-131). New York. 1936.

de Ropp, R. S. Drugs and the mind (pp. 1-310). New York. 1957.

Rusby, H. H. An examination of the properties of *Ephedra,* ephedrine and cocaine. *Druggists' Circular* #852. 1927.

—— Russian ergot. *Jour. Am. Pharm. Assoc.,* 24:383-385. 1935.

Stafford, W. E. Daturas of the Old World and New. *Ann. Rept. Smithsonian Institution,* 1920:537-567. 1920.

—— Synopsis of the genus Datura. *Journ. Wash. Acad. Sci.,* 11:173-189. 1921.

Sappington, J. The theory and treatment of fevers (pp. 1-216). Arrow Rock, Mo. 1844.

Schwarting, A. E., and Hiner, L. D. Study of domestic ergot of wheat and rye. *Journ. Am. Pharm. Assoc.,* 34:11-16. 1945.

Scott, J. The mandrake root (pp. 1-224). London. 1946.

Shepard, C. C. Capreomycin activity against experimental infection with Mycobacterium leprae. *Science,* 16 October 1964, 403-404. 1964.

Shepherd, D. A., *et al.* A synthesis of Progesterone from Ergosterol. *Journ. Am. Chem. Soc.,* 77:1211-1213. 1955.

Schwartzman, G. The effect of ACTH and Cortisone upon infection and resistance (pp. 1-204). New York. 1953.

Sibree, James. A naturalist in Madagascar (pp. 1-320). London. 1915.

Sievers, A. F., and Higbee, E. C. Medicinal plants of tropical and subtropical regions (pp. 1-47). Washington. 1942.

Sievers, A. F., Lowman, M. S., and Kelly, J. W. Effects of certain harvesting and mulching practices on the yield and survival of belladonna. *Journ. Am. Pharm. Assoc.,* 34:28-32. 1945.

Silverman, Milton. Magic in a bottle (pp. 1-332). New York. 1941.

Smith, E. S., and Dale, A. The Ila-speaking peoples of Northern Rhodesia, 2 vols. London. 1920.

Stockdale, J. J. Sketches, civil and military, of the island of Java (pp. 1-406). London. 1812.

Stone, A., and Himes, N. E. Practical birth-control methods (pp. 1-208). London. 1960.

Störck, A. An essay on the internal use of thorn-apple, henbane and monkshood (pp. 1-47). London, 1763.

Stuart, G. A. Chinese Materia Medica (pp. 1-556). Shanghai. 1911.

Stuhr, E. T. Manual of Pacific Coast drug plants (pp. 1-189). Lancaster. 1933.

Stuhr, E. T., Christensen, B. E., and Wong, E. Assay of Oregon ergot. *Journ. Am. Pharm. Assoc.,* 32:241-244. 1943.

Taylor, Norman. Cinchona: Quinine to You. *Fortune,* February, 1934.

—— Cinchona in Java (pp. 1-87). New York. 1945.

—— Flight from Reality (pp. 1-237). New York. 1949.

——— Narcotics: Nature's dangerous gifts (pp. 1-212). 1963.

Thompson, C. J. S. The mystic mandrake (pp. 1-253). London. 1934.

Togashi, K. External characters of the ergot. *Tokyo Bot. Mag.*, 56:74-82. 1942.

Varadarajan, P. D. Climate and soil conditions of *Rauwolfia serpentina* in India. *Economic Botany*, 17:133-138. 1963.

Verbeck, H. R. Painless childbirth in twilight sleep (pp. 1-246). London. 1915.

Warren, L. E. Pharmacy and medicine in ancient Egypt. *Journ. Am. Pharm. Assoc.* 20:1065-1076. 1931.

Wealth of India. Raw Materials (4 vols., unfinished). Delhi. 1940-1964.

Webster, J. E., Fellows, H., and Murphy, H. F. Yield and chemical composition of oil from castor beans grown in Oklahoma. *Tech. Bull. T.*, 27:1-18. 1947.

Willaman, J. J., and Schubert, B. G. Alkaloid hunting. *Economic Botany*, 9:141-150. 1955.

Withering, William. An account of the foxglove (pp. 1-207). Birmingham. 1785.

Woodbury, A. M., Walls, M. E., and Willaman, J. J. Steroidal sapogenins from the Joshua tree. *Economic Botany*, 15:78-86. 1961.

Woodson, R. E., Youngen, H. W., Schlittler, E., and Schneider, J. A., Rauwolfia: Botany, pharmacognosy, chemistry and pharmacology (pp. 1-149). Boston. 1957.

Woodward, E. F. Botanical drugs: a brief review. *Economic Botany*, 1:402-414. 1947.

Wootton, A. C. Chronicles of pharmacy (Vol. 1, pp. 1-428. Vol. 2, pp. 1-332). London. 1910.

Wren, R. C. Potter's new cyclopedia of botanical drugs and preparations (pp. 1-400). New York. 1956.

Youngen, H. W. Studies on Indian rhubarb. *Journ. Am. Pharm. Assoc.*, 33:145-149. 1944.

Youngen, H. W., Jr. Ergot—A blessing and a scourge. *Economic Botany*, 1:372-380. 1947.

Index

Abortion, 63, 65, 245
  legal, 245
  habitual, 246, 252
  spontaneous, 60-61
Abreaction, 68
Absinthe, 44
Abstinence, 245
"Abyss of Divine Enjoyment," 215
Account of the Foxglove, An, Withington, 125
Acetylsalicylic acid, 200
Aconitum Napellus, 43
Acokanthera, 184-185
  deflexa, 184
  schimperi, 184
Acosta, Christoval, 139
Acosta, Joseph de, 11
ACTH, 236, 238
Addison, Thomas, 228-229
Addison's disease, 229, 235-236
Adrenal cortex, hormones of the, 229-231, 244
Adrenal glands, 229-232, 236
Adrenalin, 109, 230
Africa, 2, 37, 75, 173, 253
  tropical, 175, 181, 233-234
Agar, 170
Agave, 243
  fourcroydes, 243
  sisalina, 243
Ague, 74
Air sickness, 150
Alcohol, 48, 57, 110, 150
Alexander the Great, 75, 153-154, 158
Alexandrian senna, 161-162

Alkaloids, 14, 24, 38-39, 47, 50, 55-57, 87, 91, 105, 107, 135, 138, 140, 142-147, 150, 252
  belladonna, sources of, 147-148
  of ergot, 60-65
  of opium poppy, 212-213, 216-217
Allamanda, 38, 184
Allium, 206
Alloch, 158
Aloe barbadensis, 159
  ferox, 159
  perryi, 159
  vera, 159
Aloes, 154-155, 158-160
Aloin, 160
Amazon Valley, 2, 5, 190
American Stock Exchange, 245, 248
American wormseed, 46
Amebic dysentery, 46, 49-51
Amphetamine, 110
Anchar, 175
Ancient Civilizations of the Andes, Means, 8
Andean miracle, 4-18
Andes, 2, 5-13, 190
Anesthetic, ancient, 137-138, 147
  local, 15, 17
Angina pectoris, 216
Anopheles mosquito, 77-78
Antiarin, 178
Antiaris toxicaria, 177
Anti-fertility pill, 147-252
Antirrhinum, 206
Antsjar, 175
Aperient, 155

Aphrodisiac, 140
Apocynaceae, 21, 38, 40, 179, 182
Apocynum cannabinum, 184
Applezweig, Norman, 232, 237, 241
Aralen, 99
Argot, 59
Aristotle, 158, 208, 245
Arrow poisons, 38, 42-43, 130, 172-
    175, 177-178, 181-182, 184-185,
    190, 192-195
Arrow Rock, Mo., 88
Artemisia, 44-45
    cinna, 44-45
    maritima, 45
Arthritis, 200-201, 205, 235
Asiatic toad, 130
Aspirin, 37, 200-202, 253
Asthma, 106, 108, 140, 150-151, 236
    bronchial, 109-110
Athletes foot, 199
Atlanta, 13
Atropa acuminata, 143
    Belladonna, 141-144, 147-148
Atropine, 65, 142-148, 150, 213
Auricular fibrillation, 87
Australia, 32, 144-145
Autumn crocus, 202-206
Avicenna, 54-55, 161, 210, 253
Avignon berry, 169

Babies by Choice or by Chance, Gutt-
    macher, 245
Balsam of Peru, 52, 79
Banks, Sir Joseph, 117, 203-204
Barbasco, 239
Barbiturates, 57, 111
Basel, Switzerland, 211
Bein, H. J., 24
Belladonna, 65, 134
Belladonna alkaloids, chief sources
    of, 147
Benzedrine, 110
Benzoic acid, 53
Benzoin, 52-53
Bernard, Claude, 192-195
Birmingham, England, 115-117, 120-
    121, 124, 126-128
Bitter aloes, 159-160
Bitter purge, 158-160

Bleuler, Eugen, 20
Blindness, 186
Blow pipe arrows, 193
Bolivia, 8-10, 89-90, 92
"Botanic Garden, The," 117, 175-
    176
Botanical Arrangement, Urthering,
    120-122, 126
Boussingault and Roulin, 191
Bran, 170
Brazil, 49, 90, 194
Brigham tea, 101-103, 105
Brodie, Sir Benjamin, 191
Bronchial asthma, 109-110
Bronchitis, 53
Browning, Elizabeth Barrett, 211
Brown-Sequard, Charles, 229
Brucine, 48
Buerger's disease, 216
Buitenzorg Botanical Garden, 20, 90
Bursitis, 235
Buttonbush, 51

Caffeine, 55-57, 135, 213
Calabar bean, 111, 187-189, 196
Calabash, 173-174
Calabash curare, 192-194
Camphorated opium tincture, 208
Cancer cure?, 38-40
Canvane, Peter, 164-166
Car sickness, 150
Carney, Msgr. F. W., 250
Cascara sagrada, 167-169
Cassia, 162
    acutifolia, 162
    angustifolia, 162
    Fistula, 162
Cassia bark, 163
Castor oil, 154-155, 164-166
Castor oil plant, 165
Cat units and digitalis, 130
Cataract, 15
Catharanthur roseus, 38
Catharsis, 154
Cathartic racket, 152-170
Cathartics, 153-155, 157, 160, 164, 166-
    169
    bulk, 169-170
Cattle, 232

Caventou, Joseph, 87-88, 252
Century plant, 242
Cephaelis Ipecacuanha, 50
Cephalanthus occidentalis, 51
Cerbera tanghin, 179
Cerberin, 180
Chalchupa, 22
Chandrá, 20
Charles II, 84-86
Chaulmoogra oil, 222-227, 253
"Chemistry of Madness," 70
Chen, K. K., 103, 106-107, 110-112, 252
Chenopodium ambrosioides anthelminticum, 46
Childbirth, 58-63, 149, 247
Chills and fever, 74
Chinchon, Countess, 79
Chinese medicine, 103, 155
Chinese rhubarb, 154-157
Chloropromazine, 25
Chondodendron tomentosum, 194
Chromosones, 206
Chronica del Peru, Cieza de Leon, 6, 190
Chrysanthemum, 44
Cicero, 75
Cieza de Leon, Pedro de, 6, 11, 190
Cinchona, 22, 79-87, 89-98
Cinchona ledgeriana, 96
Cinnamomum Cassia, 163
Citrullus colocynthis, 169
Claviceps purpurea, 59
Coca, 5-18
  and Coca Cola, 13
  cocaine content of, 14
  in Paris, 11-13
Coca et ses applications therapeutiques, La, 13
Coca Cola, 13
Coca museum, 12
Coca de Pérou, La, 11-12
Coca wine, 12, 16
Cocada, 8
Cocaine, 14-18, 135, 213, 253
  in coca, 14
Cocaine addicts, 16
Cocal, 10
Codeine, 213, 215-217

Coffea arabica, 55
Coffee, 54-57
"Coke," 13
Colbert, J. B., 49
Colchicine, 205
  action on chromosomes, 206
Colchicum autumnale, 203-204
  luteum, 203
Coleridge, 211
College of Physicians and Surgeons, Columbia University, 58
Colocynth, 169
Colombia, 190
Columbia University, 58
Common cold, 108, 151
Complete heart block, 108
Compositae, 44
Conception, 137, 245
  prevention of, 246-252
Congestive heart failure, 129
Constipation, 153, 161, 166
  imaginary, 153
Continence in marriage, 245, 249-252
Contraceptive, 245-252
Convallaria majalis, 42
Cooke, Helena, 119-120
Corkscrew willow, 198
Corn, 206
Corn poppy, 209
Corsica, 12
Cortex, 229-231
Cortical hormones, 230-232
Corticotropin, 236
Cortisone, 37, 182, 230-239, 244
Costa Rica, 32
Coughs, 51, 53, 216
Countess' Powder, 79
Crack willow, 198
Creeping myrtle, 38
Cromwell, Oliver, 75
Croup, 53-54
Crucifixion, 138, 143
Cuca, 8, 11
Cucumber, 169
Curacao aloe, 159
Curare, 25, 46-48, 190-196
  relaxant action of, 47, 194-195
Curarin, 191
Cuzco, 6-8

Damien, Father, 219-220
Dammerschlaf, 149
Daniell, Dr., 186-188, 253
Darwin, Charles, 116, 175
Darwin, Erasmus, 116-117, 120-121, 126, 175-178
Darwin, Robert, 116
Datura Stramonium, 134, 139-141, 147-149, 206
Dauphin, the, 49, 85-86
DDT, 99
Deadly nightshade, 134, 141-145, 147
De Foe, 206
de la Chaise, Père, 49
Delirium tremens, 48, 67, 150
De Lugo, Cardinal John, 80-81, 252
Dementia praecox, 20
De Quincey, 211, 215
de Ropp, R. S., 26, 67n., 70
Desert tea, 101
Devil's-apple, 137
D'Husson's Eau Medicinale, 204
Diaphoretic, 206
Diaphrams, 245
Digitalis, 37, 41-42, 123-132, 178, 181, 183, 185-186, 236
Digitalis purpurea, 123, 128, 130
Digitoxin, 131
Dioscorea, 238-244, 246, 248, 251
villose, 238
Dioscorides, 137, 142, 144, 169, 197-198, 202, 204, 208, 210, 253
Diosgenin, 239-242, 244
Diosynth S. A., 241
Distended abdomen, 187, 189
Diuretics, 41, 129
"Dr. Sappington's Pills," 88
Dogbane family, 21, 38, 179, 181-185
Donovan, W. J., 72
Dover, Thomas, 206-207
Dover's powder, 206-207
Dropsy, 40-41, 121-126, 129
Drousy syrup, 210
Drug addicts, 16, 69, 215
Drug seekers, 34-71
Drugs and the Mind, 26, 67n., 70
Duboisia, 145, 147-148
Ductless glands, 230
Dürer, Albrect, 75

Dutch quinine monopoly, 22, 72-73, 75, 95, 98-99
Dysentery, 49
amebic, 46, 49-51

East Africa, 185
Ebers, G. M., 153
Ebers Papyrus, 40-41, 153-154, 203, 208
Ecballium elaterium, 169
Ecuador, 190, 194-195
Eczema, 160
Edema, 57, 183
Edgbaston Hall, 126-127
Egg cell, 251
Einhorn, Albert, 17
Elaterin, 169
Electro-shock treatment, 25, 195
Embryo, 251
Emetine, 50-51
Emodin, 157, 163
Emu, 144-145
Endocrines, 230
English Hippocrates, 207
Ephedra, 102-103, 106, 112-114, 252
Ephedra antisyphilitica, 102
Ephedra dislachya, 107
Ephedra equisetine, 104, 107
Ephedra gerardiana, 113
Ephedra sinica, 104, 107, 112-113
Ephedrine, 105-114
Epinephrine, 109, 230
Equisetum, 102, 107
Ergonovine, 62-65
Ergot, 59-68, 70
Ergot poisoning, 65
Ergotamine, 62, 64
Ergotaminine, 62
Ergotism, 61-62, 65
Ergotoxine, 62
Erotic drive, 246, 252
Erythroxylon Coca, 11
Esere, 186-187
Essence of coca, 14-17
Estrone, 244
Eykman, J. F., 20

Failing heart, 129
Fairchild, David, 223

False hellebore, 43
Family Life Bureau, New York, 250
Fantus, Bernard, 152, 164-165
Faure, 12
Female sex hormones, 244, 247
Fetus, 251
Filipendula rubra, 198
  Ulmaria, 198
Fish poisons, 144, 238
Flacourtiaceae, 223
Food and Drug Administration, 29, 34-36, 247
Foxglove, 36, 42, 121-132
Foxglove cultivation, 36
Franklin, Benjamin, 117, 133
Fraser, T. H., 185, 188
Frémont, Captain J. C., 243
Freud, Sigmund, 14, 253
Friar's balsam, 51-54
Fuchs, Leonard, 122-123

Gaedeke, Dr., 14
Galen, 137, 144, 210
Gametocytes of *Plasmodium,* 77
Gangrene, 65
Garcillasso de la Vega, 6, 10-11
Garden rhubarb, 155-157
Gause, C. J., 148-149
Gerarde's *Herbal,* 138
Gerstner, Father, 234
Glaucoma, 186, 188-189
Gnetaceae, 102
Golden shower, 162
Gounod, 12
Gourd curare, 192
Gout, 197, 202-206, 236
Grass pollen, 109
Grassi, G. B., 77
Great Inca, 7
Greshoff, M., 20
Guarana, 57
Guatemala, 22-23, 32, 242
Guttmacher, A. F., 245
Guy's Hospital, London, 228

Habitual abortion, 246
Hallucinogenic drug, 66, 69
Hanbury, Sir Thomas, 158

Hansen, G. A., 220
Hansen's disease, 221
Harun al-Rashid, 161
Hasskarl, J. G., 90
Hay fever, 104, 108-110, 143, 151
  pollens and, 109-110
Heart disease, 41-43, 87, 129-132, 185, 216, 235, 252
Heidelberger, Michael, 233
Helpful poisoners, 171-196
Helvetius, Claude Adrien, 49
Helvetius, Jean Adrien, 49
Henbane, 134, 146-148
Henequen, 243
Hepatitis, 236
Herbarii Amboinensis, 21
Hermodactylus, 203-204
Herodotus, 152
Heroin, 111, 216-217
Hevea, 206
High blood pressure, 9, 29-31, 43, 107
Hindu whores, 139-140, 143, 149
Hippocrates, 138, 151, 211
History of Plants, Theophrastus, 208
Hodgkin's disease, 39, 64
Hogs, 232
Hohenheim, A. T. B. von, 211
Holmes, Oliver Wendell, 71, 154
Holy bark, 166-169
Homer, 173, 208
Hormona Laboratories S. A., 240
Hormones, 243, 253
  of the adrenal cortex, 229-231, 244
  pregnancy and, 246
  sex, 237-238, 244, 246-247, 252
  steroid, 236, 241-242
  synthetic, 244
Hormosynth S. A., 240
Horse doping, 214
Horsetail, 102, 107
Hosack, David, 58-71
Humboldt, Baron von, 191
Huxley, Aldous, 66, 69
Huxley, Sir Julian, 68
Hydnocarpus anthelmintica, 224
Hydnocarpus oil, 224
Hydnocarpus wightiana, 224
Hydrocortisone, 235-236

Hyoscyamine, 146-148
Hyoscyamus niger, 146-147
Hypo, 175

Iceland poppy, 209
Imaginary constipation, 153
Impregnation, 245, 247
Inca Roca (1250-1315), 7
Incas, 5-12, 18, 78
India, 19, 24-26, 29, 31-32, 93, 139,
    156, 162, 169, 221
  malaria in, 20, 75, 90
  population control in, 248
Indian hemp, 184
Indian senna, 162
Indonesia, 100
Infertility, 252
Institute of France, 213
Insulin, 25
Intestinal worms, 45-46
Ipecac, 49-51
Ipoh, 175

Jacobs, W. A., 233
Jahiah-Eben-Masawaih, 161
Jalap, 155
Jamestown weed, 139
Java, 20, 90-91, 93-98, 100, 175-178,
    182
Jerusalem balsam, 51
Jesuit's drops, 51
Jesuits' powder, 80-86
Jimsonweed, 139-140, 145, 147
John XXIII, Pope, 249
Joint-fir family, 102
Joshua tree, 243
Joshua tree National Monument, 243

Kei-Apple, 223
Kelly, Msgr. G. A., 250
Kendall, E. C., 230, 253
Kendall's compound E, 230
Kew Gardens, 117, 202
Kina Bureau, 98-99
Kline, N. S., 27
"Knockout drops," 146
Kola nut, 57
Koller, Carl, 14-16, 253
Kombi, 182, 184

Lo Mortola garden, 158
Lasagna, L., 35-36
Laudanum, 211
Laveran, C. L. A., 76
Lavoisier, Antoine, 117, 133
Laxatives, 154
Ledger, Charles, 92
Ledger, George, 93
"Legal" poisoning, 172
Lennox, W. G., 63-64
Leper colonies, 220, 225-227
Leprosy, 220-227, 253
Leukemia, 39-40, 236
Levant wormseed, 45
Lily-of-the-valley, 42
Lima, 2, 4, 78-80
Linnaeus, 46-47, 55, 79, 120-121, 123,
    209
Livingstone, David, 181-182, 253
Lobotomy, 25-26
Local anesthetic, 15, 17
Locomotor ataxia, 214
Locusta, a Roman poisoner, 142
Loganiaceae, 46
Los Angeles Planned Parenthood
    Center, 246
Louis XIV, King, and a quack, 48-51,
    85-86
"Lover of the Plants," Darwin, 175
Low blood pressure, 108
LSD, 66-71
Lunacy, 19-20
Lunar Society, 116, 127
"Lyric of India, A," 74

Macbeth, 27
Madagascar, 175, 178-180, 182
Madagascae periwinkle, 38, 40
Madder family, 55
Mahuang, 104-107, 155
Malaria, 33, 73-90, 252
  cause of, 75-78
  in England, 82-86
  in India, 20, 75, 78, 90
  in Rome, 74, 80
  in the U. S., 75, 99
Male sex hormones, 244
Mandragora officinarum, 136-139, 147
Mandrake, 133-134, 136-138, 145, 147

Marco Polo, 105, 156-157, 173, 209
Marcus Aurelius, 210
Mariani, Angelo, 12, 18
Marigold, 206
Markee, R. E., 237-242, 253
Markham, Clements R., 91-92
Massenet, 12
Mayo Clinic, 230-232
Means, Philip, 8
Medulla, 229-230
Menstrual cycle, 245, 247, 251
Menstruation, 247
Mental hospitals, 24-28, 195
Mescaline, 66
Mesue the Elder, 161
Metrazol, 25, 195
Mexican tea, 101
Mexico, 22, 32, 237-241
Midwives, 59, 61
Migraine, 63-65
Milton, John, 46-47
Mineral oil, 154
Moens, J. C. B., 94
Molokai, 220
Monardes, Nicolas, 10
Monkshood, 43
"Moon disease," 20, 24, 33
Moraceae, 177
Mormon tea, 101-102, 253
Morphine, 48, 57, 111, 149, 201, 209,
    212, 214-217, 236
    isolation of, 213
Mosquito and malaria, 76-78, 99
Müller, J. M., 24
Myasthenia gravis, 111, 187, 189
Mycobacterium leprae, 220

Naked ladies, 204
Napa State Hospital, 70
Nativelle, 131
Natural History of the Indies, Acosta,
    11
Neostigmine, 189, 196
Nerium Oleander, 184
Netherland East Indies, 90, 96-97,
    100, 175
Neuilly, 12
New York Botanical Garden, 12, 233
Nicotine, 213

Niemann, Dr., 14
Nigeria, 32, 187
19-norprogesterone, 246-247
Novocain, 17-18
Nux-vomica, 47-48

Oak pollen, 109
Obstetrics, 61-62
Obstructive laryngitis, 53
Oleander, 38, 42, 182, 184
Olive oil, 154
Onion, 206
    sea (see Sea onion)
Ophthalmology, 14-15, 107, 141, 151,
    189
Opium, 65, 207-218
Opium addicts, 215
Opium poppy, 209, 212, 217-218
Ordeal bean of Calabar, 188-189
Ordeal poisoners, 175
Ordeal by Tanghin, 178-181
Orellana, Francisco de, 190
Oriental poppy, 209
Osler, Sir William, 89, 215, 217
Ouabain, 183-186
Ovulation, prevention of, 247, 251
Ovules, ovum, 247, 251

Paderborn, Westphalia, Germany, 212
Pain-killers, 137, 160, 197-218
Palma Christi, 166
Paludrine, 99
Papaver nudicaule, 209
    orientalis, 209
    Rhoeas, 209
    somniferum, 209
Papaverine, 65, 213, 216-217
Paracelsus, 211
Paracus textile, 4-5, 18
Paralysis agitans, 143
Paregoric, 3, 208
Paris, 11-13, 49, 88, 133
Parkinson's disease, 140, 143, 150
Paul VI, Pope, 250
Pelletier, Joseph, 87-88, 252
Pemphigus, 236
Pen Tsao Kang Mu, 155
Penick, S. B., & Co., 37n.
Periwinkle, 38, 184

Persia, 44
Peru, 4-18, 90, 92, 190, 194-195
Peruvian Bark, 91
Peruvian marvel, 78-82
Pharmakeia, 172
Physostigma venenosum, 188
Physostigmine, 188-189
Pincus, Gregory, 246, 250, 253
Pituitary, 230
Pituri, 144-145, 147
Pius XII, Pope, 249-250
Pizarro, 6-7
Plasmodium, 76-77
Pliny, 107, 144, 146, 165, 202
Plumier, Charles, 20
Poisoned arrows, 42-43, 130, 172-175,
    177-178, 181-182, 184-185, 190,
    192-195
Poisoners, 41-48, 139, 142, 144, 149
    helpful, 171-196
    ordeal, 175
Poisonous flowers, 44-46
Pollens
    and asthma, 109
    and hay fever, 109
"Popery" in England, 82-84
Poplar pollen, 109
Poppy heads, 208-209
Poppy seeds, 217
Pot curare, 192-194
Potato family, 6, 133-151
Potato's Lethal Cousins, 133-151
Potosi, 8
Pregnancy, 189, 231, 247-252
    hormones and, 246, 252
Priestley, Joseph, 117, 127
Procaine, 17-18, 108
Progesterone, 244
Prostigmine, 111, 189
Psyllium seed, 154, 170
Puerto Rico Family Planning Center,
    246
Purges, 45, 152-155, 157-166
Pursh, F. T., 167
Pyrethrum, 44

Quacks and quackery, 2, 12, 48-51,
    82-86, 88-89, 252
Queen-of-the-meadow, 198, 200

Queen-of-the-prairie, 198
Quina, 78-79, 87
Quinidine, 87
Quinine, 22-23, 55, 73, 87, 100, 135,
    213, 236, 252
    just isolation of, 89
    synthetic, 37
Quinine consent decree, 73
Quinine factory, first in the U. S., 88
Quinine monopoly, 72-73, 75, 98-99,
    241

Ragweed pollen, 109
Raleigh, Sir Walter, 174, 190
Rat poison, 40-43, 46
Rauwolf, Leonhart, 20
Rauwolfia, 20-24, 26, 31-33
    canescens, 32
    heterophylla, 22
    serpentina, 20-23, 31-32
    tetraphylla, 21-23, 32
    vomitoria, 21, 32
Red squill, 43
Relaxant action,
    of calabar bean, 189
    of curare, 47, 192-195
    of morphine, 214
Reproductive system, 247, 251
Reserpine, 24-29, 31-33
Rhamnus infectoria, 169
Rhamnus purshiana, 167
Rheum, 156-157
    emodi, 157
    officinalis, 157
    palmatum, 157
    tanguticum, 157
Rheumatic fever, 202
Rheumatism, 198, 205
Rheumatoid arthritis, 231, 244
Rhubarb, 155-157, 252
Rhythm method, 245, 249
Richter, Gedeon, 240-241
Ricinus communis, 165
Roaring whisper, 19-33
Robinson Crusoe, Defoe, 206
Robiquet, P. J., 55
Rock, J. F., 222-224, 227
Rock, John, 250, 253
Rockefeller Center, 58

Rockland State Hospital, 27
Rogers, Sir Leonard, 227
Roman Campagna, 74, 80
Roman Catholic Church, 245, 249-251
Ross, Sir Ronald, 75-77, 252
Round worm, 44
Royal College of Physicians, 82-84
Royal Commentaries of the Incas,
    Garcilasso, 6
Rubber, 206
Rubiaceae, 51, 55
Rumpf, G. E., 20-21
Rusts, 59
Rye, 59-62, 66

Sabedra, Cristobal de, 193
Sacred bark, 167
Sagebrush, 45
St. Anthony's Fire, 59-63
St. Bartholomew's Church, Birming-
    ham, 128
St. Victor's balsam, 51
Salicin, 198-199
Salicylates, 200-202
Salicylic acid, 199-200
Salix alba, 197
Salix babylonica, 198
Salix fragilis, 198
Santonica, 45
Santonin, 45-46
Sapogenin, 238-239, 242-243
Saponin, 239
Sappington, John, 88
Sarmentocymarin, 233
Sarmentogenin, 233
Sarpagandha, 20
Scheering, 242
Schizophrenia, 20, 24-28, 30, 68
Schlittler, E., 24
Schmidt, C. F., 106-107, 110-112
Schweitzer, 49
Scilla, 40
Scopola, 147-148
Scopolamine, 145-151
Scopolia carniolica, 147
Sea onion, 40-43, 130
Seasickness, 135, 150
Seborrheic dermatitis, 199
Selkirk, Alexander, 206

Senna, 154-155, 161-163
Sertürner, F. W. A., 212-213, 252
Sex hormones, 237-238, 240, 244, 246-
    247, 252
Shakespeare, 27, 43, 138, 197, 210
Shakina palsy, 143
Sheep, 232
Shen Nung, 103, 105, 111, 114, 155,
    222, 252
Sherley, Sir Anthony, 55
Shropshire, 117, 122, 124
Sisal, 243
Skin diseases, 160, 199, 235
Small, William, 116-117
Smuts, 59
Snakebite, 22, 33
Snapdragon, 122, 206
"Snow," 16
Socotrine aloe, 158-159
Solanaceae, 134-135
Solanaceous drugs, 143-144
Son before the father, 203-204
Soothing purge, 164-166
South America, 4, 49, 173, 190-194,
    196
    (*See also* names of countries, as
    Peru)
Soy bean, 243
Spanish bayonet, 243
Spermatozoa, 247, 251
Spinal anesthesia, 108
Spiraea Ulmaria, 198, 200
Spontaneous abortion, 60-61
Spruce, Richard, 190
Squill, 40, 130
Squirting cucumber, 169
Stanley, H. M., 181
State ordeal poison, 188
Stearns, John, 59
Steroid cartel, 239
Steroid drugs, 232-233, 235-244, 246-
    248
Sterols, 232
Stevenson, R. L., 219
Stillborn births, 58
Storax, 52
Storck, Baron von, 204
Stramonium, 140
Straub, W., 178

Strophanthin, 183, 185
Strophanthus, 181-182, 184-185, 233-235, 237-238
Strophanthus gratus, 184
Strophanthus hispidus, 187
Strophanthus kombe, 182
Strophanthus sarmentosus, 233
Strychnine, 46-48, 194, 213
Strychnos, 47, 194
Strychnos nux-vomica, 47
Styrax, 52
    Benzoin, 52
    benzoides, 52
    officinalis, 52
Succulent plants (see Aloes)
Sulfone, 226-227
Sulfoxone sodium, 226
Supra-renal capsule, 229
Supra-renal glands, 230
Supression of fertilized egg cell, 251
Sweet potato, 238
Sydenham, Sir Thomas, 207, 211-212
Syntex S. A., 240-242, 248
Syntex Laboratories, Inc., 241-242
Syphilis, 101
Syrup of opium, 210

Tabes dorsalis, 214
Tagetes, 206
Talbor (or Talbot), Sir Robert, 48, 82-86, 252
Tanghin, 178-182, 188
Tanghinia venenifera, 179
Tanghinin, 180-181
Tangut, 156
Tannin, 105
Tapeworm, 44
Taraktogenos kurzi, 224
Tarragon, 45
Tea, 57
Teamster's tea, 101-102
Testosterone, 244
Tetraploids, 206
Theine, 57
Theophrastus, 208
Thevetia nerüjolia, 42
Thornapple, 139
Thyroid, 230
Tincture of benzoin, 53

Tincture of opium, 211
Tinnevelly senna, 162
Tired muscles, 187
Tobacco, 42, 134
Tonics, 48, 102
Torti, 74
Toxic and toxicum, 172
Tranquilizing drug, 26, 28-29, 110, 150
Traveller's-tree, 179
Trinity Church, Cambridge, 86
Tube curare, 192-194
Tuberculosis, 226
Turkestan, 44
"Twilight sleep," 135, 149

Uganda, 173
Ulcerative colitis, 236
Ulloa, Antonio, 89
United States, malaria in, 75
U. S. vs. 383, 340 ounces of quinine, 73
U. S. Department of Justice, 73
United States Food and Drug Administration, 29, 34-36, 247
Unwanted babies, 245-252
Upas tree, 175-178
Urari, 190
Urginea indica, 43
    maritima, 41, 43, 130
Uterine contractions, 61

"Vale of Hell," 75
van der Heyden, Herman, 81
Venetian Council of Ten, 172
Venezuela, 32
Veratrum viride, 43
Veuster, J. de, 219
Vienna, 204
Vinca, 206
Vinca minor, 184
Vinca rosea, 38-40
Virgil, 172-173

Wabayo, 184
Walnut pollen, 109
Walpole, Horace, 74
Watt, James, 116
Wedgewood, Josiah, 116

Weeping willow, 198
West Africa, 187
West Indian Aloe, 159
Wheat rust, 59
Whispers from the earth, 1-3
White willow, 197-198
Wild yam, 238
Wiley, Harvey, 34
Willow, 197-200, 202
Willow pollen, 109
Wisteria, 188
Withering, William, 41-42, 117-132, 252-253
Witheringia, 126, 128
Woorali, 190

Wooton, A. C., 55-56
Worcester Foundation for Experimental Biology, 246
Wormwood, 44

X-ray burns, 160

Yam, 238-243, 251
Yamanachi, G., 105
Yellow oleander, 42
Young, Brigham, 101, 103
Yucca brevifolia, 243
Yungas, 5

Zea, 206